A Dictionary of Medical & Related Terms

for the Family Historian

Diseases	DEFINED
Illnesses	INTERPRETED
Sicknesses	SIMPLIFIED

Epidemics	ENDURED
Ailments	ANALYSED
Symptoms	SPECIFIED
Effects	EXPLAINED

Joan E. Grundy

Published by Swansong Publications,
17, New Meadows, Upper Haugh,
Rotherham, South Yorkshire. S62 7FD

ISBN-13: 978-0-0553450-0-6
ISBN-10: 0-9553450-0-6

First published 2006

Front Cover: Electron Micrograph of the influenza virus.
Gif (colour enhanced) image plus in-line images.

Title by the same author:
History's Midwives
including a
17ᵗʰC. and 18ᵗʰC. Yorkshire Midwives Nominations Index.
Federation of Family History Societies, 2003, ISBN: 1 86006 175 3.

Printed and bound by
Q3 Digital/Litho, Loughborough,

CONTENTS

Acknowledgements   4

Explanatory Notes   5

Introduction   6

a) Basic Medical Terminology   8

b) DICTIONARY   11

c) Non-Medical Terms for Causes of Death   84

Bibliography   89

Acknowlegements

I am indebted to Dr Philip Oliver for his useful critical comments during the preparation of this publication, for his helpful information on further avenues of research and for his unfailing patience in answering my many questions.
I am also very grateful to Mrs Lynn Free for painstakingly proof reading and correcting my spelling and grammer throughout.

I gratefully acknowledge the permission given by Elsevier to use the following photographs (from the page numbers listed) in Toohey Medicine for Nurses, 1963, 6th edition, edited by Arnold Bloom of which they hold the copyright.
Pitting oedema of the legs   (page 136)
Gout   (page 512)

I am also grateful to Professor M. Stewart McNulty formerly of the Department of Veterinary Science, The Queens' University of Belfast, Stormont, Belfast, BT4 3SD Northern Ireland, for permission to use his Electron Micrographs of animal viruses – Gif (colour enhanced) image plus in-line images of the Influenza virus – copyright 1994, for the front cover of this book.

My especial thanks go to David Jepson who has prepared the layout and added the illustrations and I thank him for his support throughout the preparation of this book.

Explanatory notes

Following the Introduction, Part a) is a list of some basic prefix and suffix terms for anatomy and physiology.   Also included are some Latin terms for several organs and systems of the body which often bear no resemblance to today's English terminology.

Part b) is the Dictionary of diseases, medical and related terms that may be found when reading old documents. For many of the diseases I have given, in italics, an explanation of the symptoms and occasionally the gory descriptions taken from original 18[th]C and 19[th]C medical texts. These comments help to emphasise what our ancestors had to endure before antibiotics, painkillers and anaesthesia were introduced.

After the Dictionary, Part c) comprises terms that have no medical meaning but sometimes refer to the manner of death rather than the cause. It was not always compulsory for a doctor to be present at death or to sign a certificate of death and so the accuracy of the observations from the non-medically qualified informants leave a lot to be desired. In these cases I have tried to interpret what would have been the medical cause of death.

Introduction

This publication is intended to help the growing number of family historians, from diverse backgrounds, to interpret new and old medical and related terms. Even fifty years ago the writers of documents detailing causes of death and books describing illnesses did not have the benefit of today's medical knowledge and the terms used were sometimes more descriptive than medical.

As a nurse during the past 40 years, I have seen many changes in health care in a National Health Service which was only 13 years old when I joined. I have always been confident that my patients have had the best care available at the time and fortunately have always had the benefit of antibiotics, antiseptics and anaesthaesia.

But what of our ancestors? How did they cope with illness? Whilst reading this book in your comfortable surroundings, remember that our ancestors lived very different lives even only fifty years ago. Modern films, television and novels usually like to portray historical figures leading well nourished, healthy, clean-shaven lives. In reality nutrition depended on the vagaries of the harvest and cleanliness was not important when all the water had to be carried from a well or the river. Prior to the 20thC. there was no childhood, for children helped around the house as soon as they could walk. They were working in adult situations from as young as seven years old where they were prey to more accidents and diseases. Poor nutrition led to the prevalence of many diseases as their malnourished bodies could not fight off an infection.

Surgical operations have been performed for many centuries but until the discovery of reliable anaesthetics in the 1840's and antibiotics in 1911 many people would have died from the shock of the procedure or from infection afterwards. In the early 19thC. infant mortality was 50% and vaccinations for diseases which killed, such as measles, mumps, influenza, typhoid, polio etc., were not discovered until the late 19thC. Today, smallpox and polio have been eradicated in Europe as had tuberculosis until very recently.

The observations of early medical men were very thorough as they tried to determine the cause of diseases. They listed every symptom that patients described and compared them with their colleagues' cases. However, despite being very good at recognising symptoms they had little understanding of the causes and had relatively few effective treatments to offer. Until the 19thC. treatment of disease was a result of trial and error and if a remedy worked for a few cases it was continued for all. Today's doctors rarely see many of the symptoms described in this Dictionary as advances in the understanding of anatomy, physiology and the causes of disease has led to earlier and better diagnosis. People now have easier access to health care and therefore attend the doctor's surgery at the first sign of ill health. A diagnosis is usually made at an early stage of the disease before many of the symptoms have had time to appear and swift use of antibiotics, painkillers, surgery and other medical interventions ensures that the patient is kept comfortable and the disease kept under control even if not completely cured.

When trying to decipher what is written on your document or in your book remember the trouble you have had tracing your surname with all its variant spellings. Medicine is no different and the diseases described have just as many variations as your surname. A(r)chitis is a version of rachitis which is rickets; cardiac failure due to 'faulty infiltration' should read 'fatty infiltration of the liver'.

I do hope this dictionary will help some of you to decipher your old documents, as well as entertain you all in the process and above all give you some insight into the lives and deaths of your ancestors and finally put yet more 'flesh on the bones'.

Memento Mori – a reminder of your mortality

Joan E. Grundy
Rotherham 2006

Medical Snippets
To shed tears when diseased, is a favourable sign;
but to weep without cause is unfavourable.
The Aphorisms of Hippocrates, translated into Latin and English
by Thomas Coar, 1822, Valpy, London; reprinted 1982,
The Classics of Medicine Library, New York.

Basic Medical Terms

abortivus	premature birth.
abortus	a miscarriage.
acute	rapid onset and short duration of a disease.
amputation	removal of a limb or organ.
carpal	wrist.
chronic	long lasting or frequent recurrence of a disease.
congenital	a condition existing at birth either from a defect ocurring during the formation of the foetus or a disease acquired from the mother through the blood supply.
corporo uteri	the opening of the cervix or neck of the womb through which a baby is born.
cranial	skull.
digits	fingers or toes.
....ectomy	cutting out (suffix).
ectopic	extra or outside.
endo....	within or lining (prefix).
endemic	term applied to a disease which is present in an area all the time but will occasionally become epidemic.
epidemic	a disease which affects a large number of people in a particular area at one time.
....itis	inflammation.
gastric	stomach.
glottis	opening into the windpipe at the back of the mouth.
haem....	blood (prefix).
hepatic	liver.
hydro....	water (prefix).
hyper....	above (prefix).
hypo....	under (prefix).
inter....	between (prefix).
intra....	within (prefix).
lientery	spleen.
macerated	softened by soaking.
meatus	entrance.
mega....	prefix denoting largeness.
metabolism	the physical and chemical processes by which a living body is maintained in a state of health.
micro....	very small (prefix).
myocardial	heart.
naso-pharynx	the upper part of the throat lying behind the nose.
pandemic	an epidemic which affects a vast area such as a whole country or continent at any one time, an example being the influenza pandemic between 1918-20. There were 700 million cases worldwide and 20 million deaths which was more than the casualties of the First World War. In 1957, another pandemic caused 10 million cases in the U.K.
pulmonary	lungs.

8

opthalmic/optic	eye.
....otomy	incision of (suffix).
para....	near or around (prefix).
pes	foot; pes planus – flat foot; pes cavus – extreme arch with deformed toes.
poly....	much or many (prefix).
pyo....	pus (prefix).
rectum	the last part of the large intestine or bowel.
retro....	behind (prefix).
stenosis	narrowing or constriction of a space or tube.
sub-acute	mild form of any disease.
tarsus	instep of the foot with seven metatarsal bones.
toxic	poisonous.
tympanic membrane	ear drum.

Medical Snippets

"The sweating sickness, which either '*mended or ended*' its victims in twenty four hours ...1550."
Mayall John, Annals of Yorkshire, 1878, (page 49)
Simpkin, Marshall and Co., Leeds.

abdominal apoplexy death of an abdominal organ.
It is usually a condition of the small intestine and caused by a blockage or narrowing of the blood vessels supplying the area.
abdominal belt principally for ladies use during pregnancy or after childbirth.
It was worn to give support and warmth and was made from rigid material with an arrangement of buckles which could be expanded or contracted as necessary.
ablepsia absence or loss of vision.
abortion the interruption of a pregnancy before the 28th week of gestation. (see criminal abortion).
Prior to the 19thC. English law had allowed a pregnancy to be terminated legally providing it was done before foetal movements were felt (see quickening). *In 1803 the performing of an abortion became a criminal offence from the time of conception and both the pregnant woman and abortionist could be given life imprisonment. A further Act in 1861 made abortion a crime even if performed for medical reasons and was punishable by 3 years to life imprisonment. The Infant Life Preservation Act of 1929 made abortion legal in cases where it was done for the sole purpose of preserving the life of the mother. The Abortion Act of 1967 permits the termination of a pregnancy if the continuance involves physical or mental risks to the pregnant woman or child. The limit of 28 weeks was reduced to 24 weeks in 1990.*
The term was often used to differentiate a criminal act from natural occurrence i.e. miscarriage.
abscess collection of pus in a cavity due to an infection.
An acute abcess develops rapidly causing redness, warmth, swelling and pain and, until it has burst, the patient suffers a high temperature and is sometimes delirious. The infecting organisms may spread into the blood stream causing septicaemia.

acarus (see scabies).
accoucher man-midwife.
He is a surgeon with an interest in pregnancy and childbirth.
accoucheuse female midwife, a woman who attends other women during childbirth.
The licensing of midwives began in the reign of Henry VIII but no formal training was needed until the 20thC. Since the passing of the Midwives Act in 1902 no woman can practise midwifery habitually and for gain unless she is properly trained and has passed the examinations of the Central Midwives Board.
accouchment labour and childbirth.
achitis rachitis or rickets.
achorion the fungus which causes ringworm.
acidosis a condition in which there is either an over production of acid by the body or a dimunition of alkali in the blood stream.
It is usually caused by the faulty metabolism of fat. It occurs in diseases such as diabetes; the terminal stages of Bright's disease; from starvation or persistent vomiting. A mild form can occur in severe fevers especially in children. The symptoms are of general lassitude, vomiting, thirst, restlessness and the presence of acetone in the urine. If untreated the condition leads to deep unconsciousness, coma and death. Prior to the discovery of insulin in the 1920's the appearance of a diabetic coma was usually fatal.
Acidosis is also the cause of what was once known as delayed chloroform poisoning. A patient who had undergone an operation under chloroform and had come round from the anaesthesia very well, later suffered from incessant vomiting, became very drowsy, lapsed into unconsciousness and died.
acromegaly or giantism an increase in the size of the bones sometimes to massive proportions and most noticable in the jaws, hands and feet.

11

This is a chronic disease usually of middle age caused by prolonged, excessive secretion of a growth hormone. The hands become spade shaped, the lower jaw becomes markedly enlarged and projecting, the nose becomes thickened and flattened and the eyes widely separated. The tongue becomes almost too large for the mouth and the voice is harsh. The bones of the trunk are increased in size especially the upper

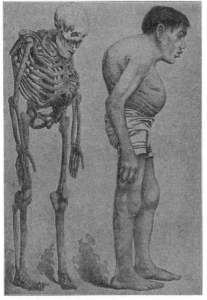

part of the spine so that the upper part of the back becomes rounded and the head is thrust forwards and downwards. The patient suffers from muscular weakness, headache and defective sight.

acute left ventricular failure rapid failure of the left side of the heart which pumps blood around the circulatory system.

It is caused by heart diseases such as chronic heart failure, heart attack, irregular heart rhythm.

Addison's disease disease of the supra renal glands, that are situated on the top of the kidneys, in which the secretions of the glands are destroyed.

The powerful secretions which these glands produce, adrenaline and cortisone, are responsible for the proper functioning of many systems of the body such as the maintenance of the blood pressure and the contractile power of the muscles. The disease was first described by Thomas Addison of Guy's Hospital in London in 1855. The main symptoms are anaemia, general languor or debility, feebleness of the heart's action, irritability of the stomach and a peculiar change of colour of the skin. The colour ranges from yellow to dark brown or even black and appears gradually but eventually covers the whole body. There follows great weakness or fainting on exertion, giddiness, noises in the ears, nausea, vomiting and occasional diarrhoea. The patient gets gradually worse although there are periods of remission. Untreated, the disease rarely lasts longer than 3-4 years and it may prove fatal within months.

adhesions usually occur after surgery when the surrounding tissues at the site of operation are inflamed, rub together and then stick together.

Eventually bands of fibrous tissue are formed and extreme pain is felt due to restriction of movement. Occasionally further surgery is performed to release the stuck surfaces.

afterbirth (see placenta).

after damp carbon monoxide gas, which is colourless, odourless and poisonous and occurs in mines.

Inhalation of the gas leads to unconcsiousness and death. If it is ignited by a spark the resulting explosion often causes fatalities.

afterpains mild uterine contractions occurring after the birth of a child.

A small piece of the placenta or a clot of blood may be retained and the womb continues to contract to assist the expulsion.

agenesis failure of, or incomplete development of, an organ or part of the body.

ague intermittent fever or malaria.
*It used to be common in marshy counties i.e.
the fens of Cambridgeshire and Essex and
was thought to be caused by effluvia from
putrid stagnating water, eating too much
stone fruit, a poor watery diet, damp houses,
evening dews, lying upon the damp ground,
watching, fatigue or depressing passions but
was in fact malaria. It was noted in the late
18ᵗʰ C. that when the inhabitants of a high
country moved into a low one they were
generally seized with intermittent fevers
which were apt to prove fatal. In the 1850's
5% of all the patients in St. Thomas's
Hospital in London were suffering from
malaria. Symptoms begin with a pain in the
head and loins, weariness of the limbs,
coldness of the extremities, stretching,
yawning and great sickness and vomiting
followed by shivering or violent shaking.
Afterwards a profuse sweat breaks out
which terminates the paroxysm. Within
minutes of being bitten by a mosquito, the
parasites it transmits have entered the liver
of the victim where they multiply in great
numbers over the next 7-15 days. The
parasites then burst out of the liver and, still
muliplying, attack and destroy the red
blood cells. At this point the symptoms of
the disease begin and if not treated the
destruction of the blood cells eventually
leads to failure of major organs and death.*
ague cake an enlarged and hardened spleen.
*This is a condition found in cases of
chronic malaria and if there is a hard knock
or blow to the abdomen the spleen will
rupture easily giving rise to a fatal
haemorrhage.*
alastrim mild form of chicken pox.
*Around 10-14 days after the initial infection
the patient suffers from fever, severe
headache and pain in the back. A rash of
blisters appears on the 3ʳᵈ or 4ᵗʰ day on the
wrists, forearms and face and with their
appearance the fever abates. As the blisters
dry they form scabs but do not leave scars
like chicken pox.*

albumin a protein which thickens when
heated, the substance in egg white.
albuminuria the presence of albumin in the
urine.
*This substance passes from the blood into
the urine when the blood pressure within the
renal veins is increased due to inflammation
of the kidneys, as the result of diseases of
the circulatory system or from infections of
the bladder. It sometimes occurs in
pregnancy and in people suffering from high
blood pressure or diabetes. It denotes
possible kidney disease.*
alpenstich pneumonia.
*This is a term used when the illness affects
persons living in high, cold regions.*
ambulatory fever a very mild fever which
does not cause any indisposition to the
patient.
*It occurs especially in typhoid fever and the
patient becomes a source of infection
to close contacts.*
amyloid disease waxy or lardacious
degeneration consists of a grey wax like
infiltration of the tissues of organs such as
the liver, bowel, kidneys and spleen.
*This is never a primary disease but is
always the end result of a longstanding
condition such as tuberculosis of the bone,
joints or lungs; ulceration due to syphilis;
cancerous cachexia or mercury poisoning.
There is a steady loss of strength, increasing
anaemia and the liver becomes enlarged
and pale with loss of function. The bowel
walls become thickened and swollen,
digestion is impaired and severe diarrhoea
occurs. The kidneys begin to fail and the
condition is always fatal.*
anasarca (see dropsy) generalised
accumulation of fluid throughout the body.
anaemia lack of red corpuscles or
haemaglobin in the blood which carries
oxygen to the body.
*It is not a specific disease but usually a sign
of an underlying disorder such as internal
bleeding from the digestive tract or uterus;
inadequate intake or malabsorption of*

13

vitamin B12, folic acid or iron; dysfunction of the bone marrow where red cells are made; or diseases such as liver and kidney failure, cancers or rheumatoid diseases. Anaemia may be present for several years without symptoms but pallor, listlessness, tiredness, depression, sore tongue, breathlessness and difficulty in swallowing will gradually occur and, if untreated, will eventually cause death.

anencephaly severe congenital malformation of a foetus in which the top of the skull and the brain are missing.
The condition is often accompanied by spina bifida.

aneurysm abnormally dilated section of a blood vessel.

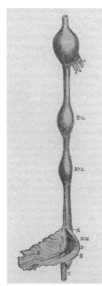

The two commonest causes are injury and disease. The Great War produced a very large number of injury aneurysms of various kinds. If a bullet or piece of shell grazed the wall of a blood vessel the wall was weakened. After a time there was apt to be bulging in the area. Thus aneurysms were found by military surgeons all over the body wherever the casualty had been hit. Such aneurysms are not likely to prove fatal as if one vessel goes out of action, other smaller vessels open up and grow wider and so carry on the circulation. Aneurysms in the aorta however could not be dealt with in this manner until surgery was developed for their treatment in the $20^{th}C$.. The patient had to lead a very quiet stress free life sometimes spending many months bedridden and avoiding all muscular strain whatsoever. The rupture of the aorta can lead to death within minutes.

angina choking.
It applies to swellings of the throat which cause difficulty in breathing such as quinsy, croup, scarlatina, laryngitis etc. There are suffocating, severe cramp-like pains occurring in spasms.

angina pectoris chest pain behind the breast bone radiating to the left jaw, shoulder or arm.
It is caused by an inadequate blood supply to the heart by a spasm of the already narrowed coronary arteries due to arteriosclerosis or atheroma. The pain is described as being like a constriction, tightness, burning, heaviness, or ache. It may also be associated with shortness of breath, palpitations or fainting.

ank(c)ylostomiasis an infection by the ankylosomum duodenale or hookworm, a thread like worm, which has been imported into the coal and other mines of this country.
It is also known as Tunnel Disease from an outbreak during the construction of the St.Gotthard tunnel in Switzerland in the 1870's. The disease affects miners and the organism is copiously discharged in the faeces. If the miners select any spot for their ablutions instead of using water-closets, the organism remains on the ground and infects other men. The larvae penetrate the skin and enter the veins, pass through the heart to the lungs and, escaping into the bronchi, reach the stomach and intestines by travelling up the windpipe and down the gullet. Once in the intestines the larvae moult and then mature. The adult worm takes up residence in the jejunum where it pierces the tissues and sucks the blood of its host. The site of entry of the larvae, usually under the toes, becomes intensely itchy, followed by the formation of pustules which ususally heal in 1-2 weeks. The symptoms of the disease are variable and include digestive problems, stomach pains, general lethargy and mental inertia. Some patients

14

may also suffer from a perverted appetite such as dirt or coal eating. Enormous numbers of the worms may be present and produce enough leakage of blood into the intestine to cause severe anaemia.

anthrax a bacterial infection of cattle and sheep which can be transmitted to humans via the hides and wool.
It is characterised by a spreading gangrenous inflammation commencing as a blister on exposed skin but with a peculiar hardness and strong unpleasant smell. The patient then begins to feel ill and will be feverish and, unless he/she was in robust health prior to contracting the infection, the microbes pass into the blood stream with fatal results. It was once common among farmers until the discovery of a vaccine by Louis Pasteur in 1881. However, there were 3 cases notified in 1971. There have also been cases caused by the use of shaving-brushes in which the anthrax spores have lain dormant for many months.

anthracosis (see pneumoconiosis).

antibiotic substance used to kill harmfull, disease causing bacteria.
e.g. penicillin is a mould which was first described in Scandinavia in 1911 and which was named by Sir Alexander Fleming in 1929 when he discovered its bacteria destroying properties.

antiseptic substance which inhibits the growth of organisms.

aorta the main artery of the body beginning in the left vertricle of the heart and supplying oxygen rich blood to the whole body.

aortic aneurism (see aneurism).

aortic disease of the heart could be any of the following diseases of the aorta.

aortic incompetence malfunction of the aortic valve in the left ventricle of the heart.

aortic regurgitation abnormal backflow of blood from the aorta into the left ventricle of the heart.

aortic stenosis narrowing of the aorta or the aortic valve leading to the heart.

aphasia loss of the power of speech following a stroke.
It may come on suddenly and last only a few hours due to temporary congestion or a blockage which is then dispersed. Usually it is permanent and the patient will have some mental impairment also.

aphonia loss of voice due to disease of the throat such as laryngitis or it can be caused by hysteria.

apoplexy a term used by Hippocrates meaning a stroke of sudden unconsciousness or paralysis due to a clot of blood or foreign body blocking an artery in the brain or from pressure on the brain due to rupture of an artery inside it.
The pulse is slow, the face is flushed, breathing is noisy and paralysis occurs down one side of the body. Occasionally warning symptoms prior to the stroke are present such as persistent headache, vomiting, giddiness, noises in the ears, confusion and a sense of fullness in the head. Death may occur at any time up to three weeks after the event but a slow recovery may take place, occasionally with residual paralysis remaining. In 1792 some of the causes suggested were a rich and luxurious diet, wearing any-thing too tight about the neck, viewing objects for a long time obliquely, continuing long in a hot or cold bath or an excess of venery (sex).

apostume a collection of pus as in an abscess.

apothecary chemist or pharmacist.
They made their own medicines but had no formal training and their shops were often the first place the sick poor went to buy medicines.

aphthae red patches with small shallow ulcers in the centre secreting yellowish or greyish fluid. They are found in the mouth tongue or throat of children and sometimes seen in conjunction with tonsilitis, measles or scarlet fever.
The child will be feverish and suffer from vomiting and diarrhoea. Small painful raw

areas appear at the corners of the mouth. Aphtha was noted by Hippocrates in the 5ᵗʰC. BC but over the intervening centuries has often been confused with the disease called thrush. However by 1891 the two diseases were recognised as completely separate.

aphthous stomatitis inflammation of the mucous membrane lining of the mouth caused by bacteria.
It is characterised by the formation of small vesicles surrounded by bright red margins. ⁻ᵉ vesicles soon rupture leaving small white, painful ˙ ulcers. They are ˳ situated on the inner surfaces of the lipₛ ˡ cheeks. If occurring in children, this wₓ ˡld make eating and drinking very painful and they would probably die from malnutrition.

appendicitis inflammation of the appendix – a worm like offshoot from the lower bowel.
An attack may begin with diarrhoea and vomiting, feverishness and abdominal pain and may resolve within a week or two. However usually the pain will increase and the abdomen will become hard, the fever will increase and the patient will lose weight. Sometimes an abscess will form and if this ruptures or leaks it will cause peritonitis.

arachnitis/arachnoiditis inflammation of the arachnoid membrane one of the three membranes covering the brain.

arsenic once used to treat skin or lung diseases but poisonous in large quantities.
It was sold over the counter and known as 'succession powder', it was used as a favourite means of murder well into the 19ᵗʰC. as an overdose was very difficult to diagnose.

arterial degeneration (see degeneration).

arterial thrombosis blood clot which becomes becomes lodged in an artery.
This disease is responsible for heart attacks, strokes and thrombosis in the legs and usually affects persons already suffering from atherosclerosis.

arteries blood vessels which convey blood, pumped by the heart, around the body.
Arterial blood is bright red due to the high concentration of oxygen and, if an artery is severed, the blood spurts out in jets in correlation with the beating of the heart.

arterio sclerosis degenerative changes in the walls of the arteries resulting in thickening and loss of elasticity.

arteritis sclerosis hardening and inflammation of the arteries.

asbestosis fibrosis of the lungs caused by prolonged inhalation of asbestos fibres.

ascarydes (see threadworms).

ascites (see dropsy) term applied to a collection of fluid in the abdomen.
It is not unusual for the amount to reach 2 gallons (8 litres) which then interferes with the action of the heart and the movements of respiration. It is removed by drainage through a large hollow needle but almost always recurs.

Asiatic cholera an epidemic disease originating in Asia and India many centuries ago.
In 1817 an epidemic began in Bengal which spread over a large part of British India and by 1823 had extended into Asia Minor and Russia. The disease continued to spread westwards and appeared in Sunderland, England in October 1831 and London in January 1832. Three further epidemics occurred in Europe in 1841, 1853 and 1885/6. The disease is caused mainly by drinking contaminated water but it is also present in the discharges from the bowels of infected persons and therefore spread to food by flies. It is characterised by vomiting and diarrhoea with faeces looking like rice-water, accompanied by severe abdominal cramps and resulting in supression of urine and collapse. Overcrowding in conditions of war and famine gives rise to epidemics and it can be fatal within a few hours of being infected. The bodies of cholera victims can stay warm for many hours after

death and muscle spasms can also alter the position of the body after death. *A vaccine to prevent the disease was used for the first time in India in 1894.*

asphyxia deprived of air resulting in suffocation and death.

asphyxia neonatorum suffocated at or before birth. *It is caused by the umbilical cord being pulled tightly around the child's neck; the separating of the afterbirth from the mothers womb before the child is delivered or the death or exhaustion of the mother during labour. It can also be caused by pressure on the infant's brain during delivery which damages the nervous system but the commonest cause used to be premature birth when the child was so weak and unable to draw in enough breath to inflate its lungs.*

asthenia weakness or loss of strength, debility. *Uniform exhaustion of all the systems of the body often without a specific disease. The individual is unable to bear strains or stresses and in severe cases cannot perform the ordinary functions of life. The cause can be of a nervous origin or it may be hereditary. Many cases are due to a prolonged illness such as cancer or tuberculosis.*

asthma narrowing of the airways in the lungs due to sensitivity to an allergen e.g. pollen, house dust mite, animals. *Minor attacks are characterised by a persistant cough, wheezing and breathlessness. In moderate attacks the breathlessness is more severe and there are generalised high pitched wheezes throughout the lungs. In severe cases there is extreme breathlessness and the patient cannot lie down and has to hold on to a chair or surface for support, they are unable to talk, are pale and sweating with rapid but weak pulse. If not relieved by steroids at this point, deterioration into Status Asthmaticus ensues quickly with confusion, slowing of the pulse and death. It is a condition which is still* fatal today if not treated promptly with steroid drugs.

asylum an institution for the support and education and long term care of the mentally ill who are unable to care for themseves.

ataxia a disease of the nervous system which interferes with sensation and balance. There are several causes one of which is syphilis.

In syphilis the disease may extend over many years and patients usually die from exhaustion or intercurrent disease. The interval from infection to symptoms can be anywhere between 5-15 years and begin with loss of reaction to light and gradual loss of vision, sharp pains which may be mistaken for rheumatism and difficulty emptying the bladder. Incoordination of movement occurs and when walking the legs are wide apart, the feet are raised high and brought down with a stamp, the walk is rapid with uneven steps with the eyes fixed to the ground. Numbness or tingling or loss of sensation in the limbs is followed by sudden violent gastric pains accompanied by nausea, vomiting and great prostration. Severe sudden pains can also occur in the bowel causing diarrhoea, in the throat causing shortness of breath and also bronchial, kidney and bladder pains. Eventually the patient becomes paralysed and bedridden.

atelectasis 1. failure of the lungs to expand at birth and the child will usually be stillborn. **2.** can be aquired after an infection or a pulmanory embolism when only a lobe of the lung collapses.

(1) Attempts at resucitation of an infant are only partially sucessful and a portion of the lung remains unexpanded. Although the child may live for a few days there is cyanosis which gradually deepens and death takes place from asphyxia, exhaustion or convulsions.

atheroma deposits of porridge-like swellings of insoluble fat on the walls of arteries.

A cumulative effect of these swellings eventually makes the arteries too narrow to preserve a good blood supply around the body.

atherosclerosis narrowing of the arteries due to fatty deposits or plaques.

This disease can often begin in child- hood and the process develops gradually over many years. The plaques build up inside the walls of the arteries and may rupture causing a blood clot to form. The repeated cycle of the build up of plaques, rupture and the formation of blood clots cause the coronary arteries to narrow leading to ischaemia and heart failure. The plaques are caused by smoking, stress, raised cholesterol or raised blood pressure.

atresia failure of foetal development, during pregnancy, of an opening in a natural passage e.g. the bowel or oesophagus.

It is fatal unless surgery is performed soon after birth.

atrial fibrillation (see auricular fibrillation).

atrophy 1. wasting of cells, tissues or organs of the body.

It is usually associated with advancing age or chronic disease.

atrophy 2. when applied to children, was another name for gastric catarrh.

Characterised by chronic vomiting of mucus and diarrhoea. The child would gradually become malnourished and die from exhaustion or from a secondary disease.

auricular fibrillation irregular heartbeat when the lower chambers of the heart do not beat in synchrony with the upper chambers.

A patient known to be suffering from heart trouble may take a sudden turn for the worse and become exceedingly breathless with swollen dropsical feet and may look and feel extremely ill. If the pulse is taken it will be found to be tremendously irregular with big and small, long and short beats all wildly jumbled together. The disease has been recognised for hundreds of years but

until the late 19^{th}C.. no one knew how the heart actually worked.

autoimmune disease the body's immune system protects it against certain diseases, bacteria, viruses etc. With an autoimmune disease the system attacks the body rather than protecting it. *It is only during the last 30 years that diseases such as pemphigus have been recognised as autoimmune.*

bacteria or microbes as they were first called are single cells of living organisms which are only visible under a microscope.

They are prevalent in all life forms either plant or animal and although some need air to survive some do not. There are three main types, round (coccal), rodlike (bacillary) and spiral (spirochetal) and all have the power to multiply rapidly and cause differing diseases. Bacteria were first identified in 1687 after the invention of the microscope but were not associated with disease until the late 1880's. They are always present on the skin but can enter the body from a wound and once in the body they deprive tissues of a great portion of their normal essential nutrients. The tissues are starved and atrophy as the nutrients that are left are insufficient for their existence. Microbes produce secretory matters which produce abnormal conditions in the tissues such as softening or coagulation and eventually destroy them. These products of change enter into the bloodstream and act as poisons on the body's systems or the bacteria live in the blood, multiply and starve, poison or decompose it.

bagassosis lung disease.

This is caused by the inhalation of dust from bagasse which is broken sugar cane after the sugar has been extracted from it. Bagasse contains 6% silica and is used in board making. (see extrinsic allergic alveolitis).

baker's itch dermatitis of the skin caused by the irritating action of substances handled by the sufferer in the course of his occupation e.g. sugar, flour etc.

The backs of the hands and fingers and the clefts between the latter are the most frequently attacked. The disease begins with small red, raised spots which may cause intense itching. This leads to scratching and the escape of a thin watery fluid. In severe cases large raw discharging areas may arise and upon these the secretion dries to form yellow scabs or crusts which tingle or burn.

Banti's disease a combination of anaemia, enlargement of the spleen, haemorrhage and ultimately cirrhosis of the liver.

It was once thought to be a disease in its own right but now recognised as a group of symptoms found in two or three different diseases.

Barbados leg (see Elephantiasis Arabum).

barber's rash tinea sycosis – ringworm.

Sycosis is derived from the Greek word meaning fig and applied to the condition as the swellings have some resemblance to the fruit, particularly the granules inside a fig, which appear on the skin. The rash begins as a small scaly patch which spreads causing pus filled blisters around the roots of the hairs. The hairs themselves are invaded by the parasite and become very fragile breaking easily. The area is very inflamed and painful and the condition may last many weeks causing scarring. It is caught from infected towels or by being licked by animals but was once commonly caught from a barber's infected brush.

barber surgeon literally barbers who also worked as surgeons, they had no qualifications, little knowledge of anatomy and worked in shops in towns or villages.

The Company of Barber Surgeons was formed in 1308 in England, and the Barber Surgeons of Edinburgh received its Seal of Cause (Charter of Privileges) on July 1st 1505 making this College one of the oldest surgical corporations in the world. The original Seal of Cause imposed a duty 'that no manner of person occupy or practice..... surgery... unless he be worthy and expert in all points belonging to the said craft'. In 1540 Henry VIII separated the two crafts declaring that 'No person using any shaving or barbery in London shall occupy any surgery, letting of blood, or other matter, except only drawing of teeth;' and surgeons were strictly prohibited from exercising 'the feat or craft of barbery or shaving'. The barber-surgeon's sign consisted of a red and white striped pole, from which was suspended a basin. The fillet round the pole indicating the riband or bandage twisted round the arm previous to blood-letting and the basin the vessel for receiving the blood.

Barlow's disease infantile scurvy.

First described in 1883 by Sir Thomas Barlow a prominent English children's doctor. Prior to this the disease had been confused with rickets.

basal meningitis meningitis in the lower part of the brain or cerebellum.

basal pneumonia infection in the lower lobes of the lungs.

It is seen usually in elderly patients who are ill and lie flat for long periods at a time.

Basedow's disease (see Graves disease).

bastard pleurisy a mild, not quite so painful, form of pleurisy.

Bazin's disease erythema induratum – slow to heal ulcers and nodules appearing in crops on the legs.

It is principally a disease of young delicate girls between the ages of 10-20 years. The girls affected are usually of a pale, flabby type with cold purplish feet suffering from tuberculosis or anaemia whose work involves standing for lengthy periods. Painless swellings, like peas, occur between the knees and ankles which slowly increase to the size of a marble. The surrounding tissue then swells and the nodules become dark red. Tenderness or itching then occurs and the nodules either become absorbed leaving a dark stain on the skin or proceed to an ulcer which takes several months to heal leaving brown coloured scars.

19

bedlam corruption of Bethlehem the name of a religious house in St. George's Field's, London which was converted into a hospital for lunatics after the disolution of the monastaries by Henry VIII.

benign harmless.

It is a term used to differentiate non-cancerous from cancerous tumours.

bile secretions of the liver, which are collected in the gall bladder before being passed into the bowel.

bilious colic (cholick) spasm of severe griping pain in the abdomen due to the passage or impaction of a gall stone in the bile duct.

The pain is caused by violent irregular contractions of the muscular tissue around the bile duct in an effort to pass a gall stone into the bowel through a narrow tube which is only meant to carry fluid. An attack usually occurs 4-6 hours after a meal at night and the pain is felt all over the abdomen and sometimes in the shoulders or back. The area over the liver is very tender and the muscles rigid. The skin is hot and profuse sweating alternating with shivering occurs along with vomiting of a greenish or frothy matter, a bitter taste in the mouth and the passing of small amounts of highly coloured urine. Between spasms, which can last for a few hours up to several days, there is a constant ache over the lower right ribs in the area of the gall bladder.

bilious fever a continual or intermittent fever accompanied by vomiting and diarrhoea.

It usually occurred towards the end of the summer and ceased at the approach of winter. In the winter of 1774 a very bad epidemic of this disease raged among the young people of Edinburgh. Accompanied by quinsy, the symptoms were so blended with others of a putrid nature that treatment of the disease was very difficult. Towards the end of the fever many patients were afflicted with large swellings under the jaws and discharges from one or both ears.

bilious vomiting digestive disorder when a patient is constipated and nauseous they are said to be bilious.

The condition is due to the incomplete digestion of food or attacks of migraine. After a night disturbed by terrifying dreams, the patients wake unrefreshed and complaining of headache and a general feeling of being weak and ill. They are irritable and unduly depressed by minor problems. On attempting to rise they feel giddy with floating specks which disturb the vision. There is a foul taste in the mouth and the skin has a sallow, muddy appearance with dark rings around the eyes. The appetite is lost and the patient feels sick. The retching or vomiting is accompanied by a cold sweat and considerable prostration, diarrhoea or constipation. Thirst is a common symptom and recovery may take many days.

biopsy small piece of living tissue taken for examination.

It is used to determine cancerous and non-cancerous tissue.

bird fancier's lung (see pigeon fancier's lung and extrinsic allergic alveolitis).

black damp the name given to the stagnant air of old mine workings from which oxygen has disappeared leaving nitrogen and carbon dioxide.

black death bubonic plague.

It was characterised by the distinctive swelling and discoloration of the lymphatic glands in the groin, neck and armpits on the first or second day of infection. It was accompanied by a high temperature, inflammation of the kidneys, internal bleeding, coma and heart failure. Death occurred in about 5 days. It is a bacterial infection caught by the bite from a rat flea then spread by coughs and sneezes. The word plague originally meant 'a blow', a reference to the speed and violence with which an epidemic occurred.

black sickness (see cerebro-spinal fever).

black smallpox the most fatal form of the disease and is so called because of the dark blue, violet or black pustules. *These are due to bleeding that has taken place into the skin and in some cases blood is lost from the nose, mouth and other orifices. Such cases are accompanied by delirium, with high fever and rapidly end in death.*

black vomit caused by the presence of blood in the stomach.
May be dark masses of vomit in cases of yellow fever or a black sediment, like coffee grounds, in cases of a bleeding stomach ulcer.

blackwater fever acute illness caused by exposure to virulent strains of malaria or by fatigue, trauma or exposure to cold in persons already suffering from malaria.
The symptoms include fever, rigor, nausea, bilious vomiting, abdominal pain and jaundice. Blood in the urine turns it pink, red or port wine coloured ('black water') and the spleen and liver are enlarged and tender. After a few hours the temperature falls, there is profuse sweating and the skin becomes jaundiced. The mortality rate varies between 10-20% but can be as high as 40%.

bladder in throat (see diphtheria).

bladder stones small concentrations of minerals and salts which form hard particles in the bladder or kidney.
They are very painful and sometimes impossible to pass with the flow of urine. An operation was often performed, without anaesthetic, to remove them.(see gravell).

blast (see erysipelas).

bleb is the same as a vesicle except in size. They can be as large as walnuts or hen's eggs and may be filled with pus.

bleeding this practice is of great antiquity and consists of an opening into a vein to let a quantity of blood freely flow depending on the strength, age, constitution etc., of the patient.
Leeches were often used to bleed patients with several being applied to the skin at

once. A hungry leech will sometimes bite more readily if it is made to crawl over a blanket first and will usually drop off the skin of its own accord when satisfied. It was considered to be the first necessary treatment of any illness or injury, from falls and bruises to fevers and childbirth.

blood life sustaining fluid which circulates throughout the body carrying oxygen and nutrients.
It was thought by the ancient Greeks to be one of the four 'humours' needed for a healthy body, a predominance of blood made a person sanguine, having a warm and passionate nature.

blood letting (see bleeding).

blood poisoning (see septicaemia).

bloody flux (see dysentery).

blue disease (see cyanosis).

boil localised infection of the skin, usually around a hair follicle, which develops into an abscess.
It is caused by infection entering the skin by means of a hair follicle. At its height a boil is a small, bright red, very painful swelling, often conical in shape surrmounted by a yellowish tip which if pricked will discharge a small amount of pus. They may occur singly or in crops and are a common feature of uncontrolled diabetes.

borborygmi flatulence.
It is the name given to the loud rumbling or gurgling noises made at times by the stomach and bowels.

botulism one of the most powerful poisonous bacteria found in foods such as sausage meat, ham, vegetables or in soil, on mouldy hay or fruit.
If ingested the toxin produces symptoms which include loss of voice, double vision, dilated pupils, difficulty swallow-ing and paralysis of the respiratory system. Death

occurs rapidly unless an antibiotic is given at the first sign of symptoms. The bacteria can only be killed at a temperature of 70 degrees centigrade sustained for an hour.
brain fever popular name for several afflictions of the brain.
Including severe mental strain caused by stress; encephalitis lethargcia or meningitis.
brain shock (see concussion).
brassfounder's ague a condition occurring in men inhaling the fumes of oxide of zinc given off during the casting of brass.
Symptoms begin with malaise, cough and throat irritation which quickly subside only to return in a few hours. Then headaches occur accompanied by nausea and vomiting, muscular pains and trembling followed by severe shiver-ing attacks. The temperature rises and attacks may last for one or two days.
breakbone fever (see dengue).
brick-dust disease the constant inhalation of brick-dust produces irrita-tion and eventual hardening of the lung tissue which leads to fibroid phthisis.
The dust formed during the manufacture of bricks is composed of a mixture of clay, sand and earth. The sand particles are sharp and angular and are the most danger-ous to the lungs. The death rate from this disease was very high among bricklayers.
bricklayer's anaemia (see anklylomiasis).
bricklayer's itch skin disease affecting mainly the hands and wrists.
The angular particles of lime scratch the skin and irritate it causing eczema which oozes clear fluid. Crusts then form and the condition becomes chronic. It is also seen in stonemasons, whitewashers and cement workers or anywhere that lime is used.
Bright's disease a term for several forms of acute and chronic kidney disease usually associated with protein (albumen) in the urine, dropsy and with various secondary diseases resulting from deterioration of the quality of the blood.

The tissues of the kidneys become thickened with fibrous tissue in diseases such as scarlet fever or pneumonia or it can occur in painters who absorbe lead from the paint. It was first described in 1827.
British cholera or simple cholera a milder form of Asiatic cholera.
bronchial catarrh mucus from a common cold settling in the lungs and possibly going on to cause bronchitis or pneumonia.
bronchiectasis condition found in patients who have suffered from long term bronchitis or chronic pneumonia.
The lungs themselves shrink while the tubes become distended into large cavities which produce copious amounts of mucus secretion which putrefies. The patient then coughs or spits up large amounts of this foul smelling mucus which renders their breath and the air of the room very offensive.
bronchitis inflammation of the large airways in the lungs and may be acute or chronic.
Chronic bronchitis is a condition of ageing and degeneration of the respiratory system caused by many years of irritation by pollutants in the atmosphere, smoking or inhaled disease causing organisms. The bronchial glands secrete excess mucus and inflammation is caused by repeated infections, and the airways gradually become narrowed. Resulting emphysema and pulmonary hypertension lead to right ventricular failure and the patient's face becomes blue, breathing is shallow and profuse quantities of infected sputum are coughed up. Any acute infection on top of chronic bronchitis will cause respiratory failure leading to increased breathless-ness, drowsiness, confusion, agitation, head-ache, a bounding and often irregular pulse, low blood pressure and eventual collapse of the circulatory system.
bronchitis kettle a tin kettle with a long spout which has a fanned end through which steam issues.

22

The kettle was used for moistening the air of the sickroom in cases of bronchitis, croup or

pneumonia. The water is kept boiling continuously either on the fire or on a Bunsen burner.

bronchocele enlarged thyroid gland in the neck. (see goitre).

broncho-pneumonia pneumonia infection affecting the tiny air sacs in the lungs.
The large bronchi are inflamed and in children the entire bronchial wall is affected. There is a high fever, rapid respirations and cough, prostration and cyanosis. Always a serious disease and fatal to small children, it usually occurs secondary to measles, scarlet fever, whooping cough, etc.

brown atrophy of the heart the affected organ is a dark brown colour due to increased pigmentation of the cells.
The condition is commonly connected with senile marasmus, wasting from inanition, tuberculosis or cancer.

brucellosis in the UK, USA and South Africa caused by drinking infected cows milk and in Malta and the Mediteranean by drinking infected goats milk.
The micro-organism is responsible for contagious abortion in cattle and farm workers, veterinary surgeons and abattoir workers are particularly susceptible. The symptoms consist of headache, sickness, loss of appetite, constipation and a feeling of tenderness over the liver and spleen, both of which are enlarged. There is a cough and a fever and the symptoms may come and go over a period of 3 months resembling typhoid.

brustyng (see hernia).

buboe swelling of the glands.
In the groin it is usually due to venereal disease gonorrhoea, on other parts of the body it is due to the plague.

bubonic plague (see black death).

bulla (see bleb).

bullous impetigo an infectious skin disease which can occur in all age groups.
The condition is characterised by painful spots with a red base which develop into a pus filled blebs. When the blebs rupture the straw coloured discharge dries forming a thick infectious crust. Additional symptoms such as fever, green diarrhoea, pneumonia, and nephritis can occur. The condition is spread easily via towels, crockery or direct contact with an infected patient.

bursitis inflammation within a bursa, a natural hollow in fibrous tissue containing a small amount of fluid.
Bursa are situated in areas of pressure or friction and they allow free movement without stretching or straining the joint. Injury or repeated pressure results in a collection of excess fluid in the bursa and the joint becomes chronically swollen, hot, red and painful.

butchers wart a term that applied to a form of lupus which occurs in those who constantly handle animal carcasses.
The disease starts where there has been an abrasion or cut on the hands through which the infection is introduced. The symptoms are a mild inflamed area that has a warty appearance at the edges.

byssinosis a form of pneumoconiosis found chiefly among cotton and flax workers.

23

cachexy severe weakness and emaciation caused by malnutrition.

caesarian section surgical operation through the abdomen to remove a baby if it cannot be delivered normally.

calculus bladder, kidney or gall bladder stones.

camp fever (see typhus).

cancer a deposit or overgrowth of cells caused by the mutation or activation of abnormal genes that control cell growth.

The rogue cells can spread indefinitely into the surrounding structures and if the lymphatic system is involved spread may occur to any distant part of the body away from the primary growth.

canine appetite an insatiable desire to eat.

canine madness (see rabies).

cancrum oris canker of the mouth a rare form of infective gangrene mainly affecting undernourished children living in squalour.

It usually occurs when the child is around 2-3 years old and recovering from an attack of measles. There is severe spreading ulceration inside the mouth leading to loss

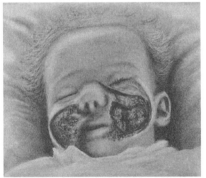

of facial tissue such as the lips, cheeks and nose. Great prostration and a high fever are followed by broncho-pneumonia which usually proves fatal. The Desmond Wilcox series of TV documentaries from 1980 – 1999 about 'The Boy David' featured this disease.

canker small ulcers which form in the mouth and on the lips as a result of local irritation such as a jagged tooth or from the deterioration of a person's general health.

capillary bronchitis acute bronchitis which affects the smaller bronchial tubes and is a usual accompaniment of broncho-pneumonia.

It is a common sequel of a common cold and occurs mainly in early spring and late autumn. The young and old are especially affected and it is a frequent cause of death in the elderly who are acutely ill from some other disease or accident. It also follows measles, diphtheria, influenza, whooping cough and scarlet fever or patients who are unable to swallow properly after a stroke when particles of food or fluid may pass into the windpipe and thence into the lungs. Cases were common after operations around the mouth and nose and in cancer of the windpipe.

carbuncle a deep-seated infection of the skin causing numerous irregular and interconnecting abscesses which discharge through multiple openings.

It begins with a hard, painful swelling of livid colour which enlarges rapidly. The pain is severe and the patient much depressed The abscesses are usually found on the back or neck and are common in 'those who indulge freely in the pleasures of the table'.

carcinoma a type of cancer growing from skin or mucous membrane which is spread by the lymphatic system allowing it to enter any lymph gland in the body.

carcinoma ventriculi cancer of the stomach.

carcinomatosis cancer which has spread throughout the body.

cardiac asthma occurs in left ventricular failure when the patient becomes very breathless with only moderate exertion.

It also occurs during the night and the patient wakes gasping for breath and has to sit up in bed or go to the window for air. The pulse is very rapid and may be irregular.

cardiac degeneration (see heart failure).
cardiac dilation enlargement of the heart due to heart failure.
cardiac dyspnoea (see cardiac asthma).
cardiac failure (see heart failure).
cardialgia denotes pain or an uneasy sensation in the stomach accompanied with anxiety.
A heated feeling sometimes attended with oppression or fainting and frequently with an inclination to vomit.
caries (1) a disease of bone in which it becomes very porous and thin as a result of chronic inflammation. (see spinal caries).
The hard calcium salts are slowly absorbed as a result of the inflamation and may ultimately be replaced entirely by soft cheesy material. When the disease attacks bones near the joints stiffness and limitation of movement results.
(2) dental caries, progressive disintegration of the teeth, is the commonest disease in the world.
caseous necrosis or death of tissues particularly in cases of tuberculosis or other chronic diseases.
Instead of turning into pus the dead cells form a cheesy like substance which hardens and becomes inelastic like scar tissue
cassion disease or 'the bends' suffered by divers who are returned from a deep dive too quickly.
The pressure underwater is much higher than on land and if the pressure on the body is reduced too quickly bubbles of nitrogen from the blood stream are released into the body causing severe pain in muscles and joints.
cataract clouding of the lens of the eye.
It is one of the main causes of blindness but now treatable by removal and replacement of the lens.
catarrh term given to mild inflammatory changes of mucous surfaces which increases their secretions.
The word is usually used to describe inflammation of the lining of the nose and

upper air passages but is also used with reference to mucous membrane lining certain hollow organs of the body. Therefore there may be catarrh of the bladder, stomach or intestine, of the bile ducts, womb etc.
catarrhal pneumonia (see broncho-pneumonia).
catarrhal stomatitis inflammation of the mucous membrane lining of the mouth.
Caused by the common cold.
catarrhal tonsillitis a highly infectious disease.
The tonsils are enlarged and covered with a whitish grey discharge. In the early stages it may be confused with diphtheria and occasionally will spread to the surrounding tissues causing an abscess or quinsy. The whole of the throat is inflamed, the tongue is covered with a thick fur and the breath often has an unpleasant smell. In children it may be the precursor of diseases such as rheumatic fever or Bright's disease.
catheter a long hollow tube usually used for draining urine from the bladder.
Its use dates back to antiquity and it was originally made from hollow reeds, stems or wood. Later ones were made from gold, silver, bronze or glass and during the 19^{th}C. from india rubber.
catheterise to remove urine from the bladder when it cannot be passed naturally.
caudel gruel mixed with wine, sugar and spices.
It is given to a woman during childbirth and after her safe delivery shared with visitors.
caul part of the placental membrane covering a child's face at birth.
Within the womb a child is surrounded by fluid enclosed in a membranous bag. During childbirth the bag ruptures and the child is born through the tear but occasionally a child is born still in the membrane or at least with the membrane over its head. This covering is known as a caul or cap and if it covers the nose and mouth the child is in danger of being suffocated or drowned and

the caul should therefore be removed immediately at birth. It was once thought that children born with this would never drown.

cellulitis inflammation of the tissues under the skin which surround the muscles, blood vessels and nerves. *Cellular tissue contains the lymphatic vessels which readily take up poisonous or septic material and convey it to the lymphatic glands which act as filters and serve to prevent micro-organisms from entering the general circulation. Cellulitis may occur anywhere in the body but is most likely to occur in the following situations. (a) Beneath the skin of the limbs as a result of infected wounds. (b) In the arm-pit following infected wounds of the hand or arm in which the infection has travelled to the lymph glands in the arm pit. (c) In the neck following severe tonsilitis or other septic throat conditions. (d) In the female pelvis arising from septic conditions of the womb following a criminal abortion.*

cerebral disease any disease of the brain.

cerebral effusion (see stroke).

cerebral embolism (see stroke).

cerebral exhaustion loss of mental power from fatigue, prolonged disease, excessive heat or cold, or mental disorder.

cerebral haemorrhage (see stroke).

cerebral palsy an old term for paralysis occurring at birth or in infancy. *There could be paralysis of one limb which would probably be caused by trauma during birth or several limbs as well as the head and neck. The likely cause of this would be congenital or from poliomyelitis.*

cerebral softening (see softening of the brain).

cerebral thrombosis (see thrombosis and apoplexy).

cerebral vascular degeneration slow deterioration of the blood vessels in the brain. *It is usually an ageing process but can be induced by a stroke or injury.*

cerebrospinal fever (see spinal meningitis).

chalicosis a form of pneumoconiosis caused by the inhalation of clay and flint particles used in the manufacture of china and earthenware. *The symptoms of a cough and gradually failing health are usually noted for some time before the patient admits to illness. The phlegm coughed up, which is generally profuse, may contain particles of the foreign matter which has been inhaled. The bronchitis and emphysema which gradually develop account for shortness of breath and wheezy condition of the patients. It is incurable although patients may live with the disease for many years.*

chancre venereal ulcers. *They can occur on the lips through kissing an infected person or on the external reproductive organs. They appear as small red itching pimples which burst and degenerate into a chronic ulcer. The base of the sore is covered in a sticky mucus and the edges slowly become hard.*

chicken pox infectious disease usually of childhood. *It is characterised by listlessness and drowsiness with no appetite but a great thirst. Patients complain of weariness and upon taking exercise break out in a great sweat. These symptoms are succeeded by alternating fits of cold and heat which become more violent and are accompanied by pains in the head and loins and vomiting. When the child drops off to sleep he awakes in a kind of horror with a sudden start which is a sign of the approach of the eruption of the pustules, a rash of red spots which become transparent blebs within a few hours. The rash appears in crops over 4-5 days on the scalp, trunk, limbs, mouth, nose or vagina. The incubation period from infection to the first signs of the disease is between 13-16 days. In young children convulsions will occur at this time. A slow eruption of the pustules and an abatement of the fever as soon as they appear signifies a favourable outcome of the disease although*

26

the scars left by the scabs of the pustules are very unsightly. They dry up in 3-4 days leaving crusts which should be left to drop off, but if picked off scarring will result. A livid brown colour of the pustules or small flat pustules with black specks in the centre is an unfavourable sign and pustules that contain a thin watery fluid are also very bad. The larger the number of pustules on the face the greater the danger and if blood appears in the faeces or urine, the abdomen swells and the patient is unable to pass urine the prognosis is very poor. A violent throbbing of the arteries is a sign of approaching delirium or convulsions.

If the tongue is coated with a brown crust, the patient is cold and shivering and grinding their teeth death is not far away.

chilblain inflammation and swelling of the hands, feet and sometimes the ears due to poor circulation, poor health and exposure to cold.

The skin becomes purple and itchy then blebs containing a thin yellow fluid form over the discoloured area and become very painful. As the blebs burst they leave behind an ulcerated surface which is very difficult to heal.

childbed labour and delivery of a child.

childbed fever a bacterial infection of the traumatised tissues occurring during or just after childbirth.

This was a well known condition for many centuries but not until 1840 was it recognised as often being caused by the birth attendants. Until this time childbirth was conducted by midwives and surgeons who had no knowledge of hygiene. They went from one delivery to another without washing their hands or changing clothes that had been splattered with blood. Trainee surgeons often went from a post mortem on a dead body, which was full of infection, to deliver a baby. A prolonged labour would leave the mother exhausted or a traumatic delivery with unwashed hands or instruments would leave the mother vulnerable to infection. Tears of the birth canal were not stitched and the mother was kept in bed for up to a fortnight after the delivery. During this time the bed linen was not changed at all. The death of women from childbed fever was very sudden and sometimes occurred in mini epidemics if the local midwife was carrying the infection. An American report of 1874 claims that women who were cheerful and smiling in the morning were quickly overcome by fever, rapid pulse, pale and shrunken features who sunk and died without a struggle before the following day. In the 1840's in Vienna, Ignas Semmelweis suggested hand washing in chloride of lime before assisting in childbirth. However it was not until the advent of antibiotics and antiseptics that the infection was brought under control. It was made a notifiable disease in England in 1919 and any midwife who has contact with the disease must notify her Local Supervising Authority.

child crowing (see laryngismus stridulus).

chin cough (see whooping cough).

chiragra old term for gout affecting the hands.

chirurgeon old spelling of surgeon.

chlorosis (see green sickness).

choke damp an evil smelling mixture of gasses containing sulpuretted hydrogen produced following the use of explosives in coal mines.

cholecystitis inflammation of the gall bladder.

cholelithiasis the formation of gall stones in the gall bladder.

cholesteatoma a cyst containing dead cells and wax usually situated behind the ear drum in the middle ear but can occur in the ear canal.

The first symptom is a repeated offensive discharge and as the cholesteatoma grows it will destroy the tiny bones in the ear causing deafness. Eventually the facial nerve is involved causing facial paralysis, dry eyes and alteration in taste. As the disease progresses vertigo becomes common. Surgery is the only treatment and if untreated can lead to meningitis or an abscess near the brain which can be life threatening.

cholera asphyxia (see Asiatic cholera).

cholera belt intended to maintain a moderate warmth over the lower part of the abdomen.

They were used to prevent any predisposition to cholera and were found useful to wear by those who had a tendency to irritation of the bowels. They were made of woollen material and bought either with buckles or in one piece to pull on.

cholera nostrus severe diarrhoea which occurs in temperate climates in the summer months.

This was probably a form of food poisoning.

cholick (see colic).

chorea a disorder of the nervous system occurring mainly in children.

The child will usually become sad, irritable and emotional and generally unwell. This is followed by restlessness and fidgety awkward behaviour. The child is never still and is very clumsy. Speech and eating are difficult and when the tongue is put out it is in a jerky manner and it is then immediately withdrawn along with a rapid closing of the jaws. The incoordinated movements of the limbs make walking difficult. The disease is a manifestation of acute rheumatism and therefore often affects the heart. In severe cases anaesthesia is required to control the violent movements of the limbs and if accompanied by sleeplessness the effects of exhaustion may prove fatal. The disease is often called Sydenham's chorea to distinguish it from Huntington's chorea which affects adults.

chorionepithelioma cancerous growth of the womb occurring after an abortion or delivery.

chronic or cold abscess usually caused by tuberculosis and takes weeks or months to develop.

It is called an abscess but instead of pus it is filled with fluid consisting of liquefied dead tissue which has undergone fatty degeneration. This type of abscess is not painful unless it presses on nearby nerves. It also tends to spread far from the original source. When a cold abscess reaches the surface of the skin there may be some redness, but this type of abscess should never be burst as the discharge will become chronic, give rise to a fever and weakness and will prove often fatal.

chronic pneumonia prolonged broncho-pneumonia causing degeneration of the lung tissue and the formation of small abscesses.

It usually occurs at the same time or after a bout of bronchitis and was common in children following an acute illness such as whooping cough or measles. Old people are particularly affected and it is one of the chief causes of death among the elderly bringing old age to a peaceful end. It was once known as 'the old man's friend' but is now treatable with antibiotics.

cimex lectularius bed bug.

This wingless, blood sucking parasite lives in cracks in walls and floors during the day and feeds on its victims at night. It is a flat, rusty brown coloured  *insect which if squashed gives off an extremely offensive smell. Eggs hatch out into larvae in 6-10 days and become adult in about 12 weeks. The adult bed bug lives for 3-6 months but can live for up to a year without food.*

cirrhosis or fibrosis in which the usual tissue of the organ is replaced by fibrous tissue similar to scar tissue whch is hard and inelastic – term usually applied to the liver, kidneys or the lungs.

The condition is incurable and will eventually lead to death as the organ ceases to function properly.

clap (see gonorrhoea).

cleft palate (see hare lip).

clergyman's throat (see pharyngitis).

club foot (see talipes).

clyster / glyster (see enema).

coal miners phthisis (see pneumoconiosis).

cold palsie hypothermia.
Prolonged exposure to extreme cold can be fatal to young and old. Blood is drained away from the extremities to the vital organs, mainly the brain, and the patient dies from a stroke preceeded by a great sleepiness.

coleis invalid broth.

colic very painful abdominal spasm. *Sometimes caused by lead or arsenic poisoning, appendicitis, intusseption, swallowing foreign bodies such as seeds of fruit or gallstones. It was common in cider making counties of England from the lead vessels used in the preparation of the cider. Also common in children due to overfeeding or gulping in of air if feeding on an empty breast or bottle, or if they have an infection.*

colloid cancer cancer of the peritoneum.
The symptoms begin with a small tumour in the abdomen which, over many months, increases in size in all directions. There is no pain and only slight indigestion or constipation. The disease is fatal and at post mortem the abdominal cavity is found to be filled with up to a gallon of soft, gelatinoous transparent fluid whicih is bright honey yellow in colour. Many of the organs such as the spleen and liver are entirely buried in this jelly and are completely unidentifiable.

coma Greek word meaning deep sleep. *The patient is insensible and unable to respond to either external stimuli or physical and mental needs.*

combined sclerosis of the cord chronic condition of the spinal cord in which parts of it become increasingly hard in consequence of the disappearance of the nerve fibres and their replacement by an overgrowth of connective tissue.
This change occurs in diseases such as locomotor ataxia or multiple sclerosis.

concussion violent shaking or agitation of the brain causing temporary paralysis of the nervous system.
It can be caused by a blow to the head or a fall.

confinement labour and childbirth.

confluent smallpox the pocks of the disease all run together and it is a very fatal form.
The symptoms are the same as smallpox but much more severe and the pocks appear on the second day. The fever is very high and continuous and as the pimples grow in size great swelling of the face is produced as they run together in large blisters. The eyelids, jaws and ears swell and there is a constant flow of saliva from the mouth and a harsh cough. The ball of the eye may be attacked and vision destroyed. There then begins a great swelling of the hands and feet due to the pustules which is accompanied by great pain. When the pustules have become ripe, full of matter, which occurs between the 11th–13th day they give out a most disgusting stench. The patient's skin is in a most serious condition with the leaking pustules, ulcers formed from them and often boils and abscesses due to the irritation of the decomposing matter of the pocks. Death is very common and usually occurs between the 11th-14th days. Excessive delirium or deep unconsciousness and much difficulty in breathing precede death which sometimes arises from suffocation by swelling and the formation of membranes in the throat.

congenital condition or abnormality existing before birth.
Although many malformations are now detected in the early stages of pregnancy, and a medical termination of the pregnancy offered to the mother, 20% of all infant deaths in England and Wales in 1980 were due to congenital malformations.

29

congenital heart disease sometimes caused when a woman catches rubella (german measles) during the first three months of her pregnancy.

The resulting abnormality to the baby's heart takes various forms such as a defect in the septum (the fibrous tissue dividing the chambers of the heart), abnormalities in the valves of the heart, a narrowing of the aorta as it enters the heart or the heart may be on the right side of the chest instead of the left.

congestion excess abnormal collection of blood in any part of the body.

Congestion of the brain is sometimes used to describe meningitis or stroke. Congestion of the lungs is sometimes used to describe broncho-pneumonia.

consumption (see tuberculosis).

contagious the communication of disease to a healthy body by actual contact with the sick or with the secretions and matter from their bodies.

contusion a bruise.

convulsions continuous or spasmodic involuntary contractions of the muscles.

They are often seen in infants with a high temperature and sometimes referred to as convulsive fits.

coronary cardiac failure (see heart failure).

corset 'female garment worn in order to produce such a configuration of the body as is a gross travesty of its natural formation (see picture) is an offence against all canons of beauty and are extremely damaging to health'.

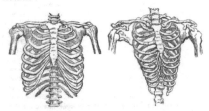

These garments were not popular with doctors who remarked that they were: 'Worn in order to hide the effects of unhealthy living and faulty habits they encourage the processes of disease in an attempt to disguise the superabundance of her adipose tissue and the flabbiness of her body producing a wasp like waist'.

coryza inflammation of the nasal passages causing sneezing, congestion and runny nose.

It is also known as the common cold.

costive constipated.

cow pox a disease in which blisters form on the udders of cows.

It is transferable to humans but persons infected rarely suffered afterwards from smallpox. This formed the basis for Edward Jenner when he began his experiments in vaccination in 1796.

cradle cap seborrhoeic dermatitis which affects the scalp of babies or children.

The oil forming glands of the skin do not function properly giving rise to an accumulation of dry skin or dandruff. In severe cases the scalp becomes inflamed with a profuse discharge and the dermatitis spreads to the forehead, eyebrows and back of the neck.

creeping paralysis also known as softening of the brain.

The term is used in the terminal stages of syphilis when mental deterioration occurs before death.

crepitus the grating sound which is heard when the ends of fractured bones rub together or in chronic arthritis when the dried internal surfaces of the joints rub together.

cretinism
congenital dysfunction of the thyroid gland causing impaired mentality, small stature and coarseness of skin.

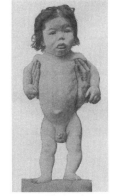

If treated with thyroid extract, good improvements may be seen.

criminal abortion forced delivery of a foetus or the products of conception.
Unqualified medical practitioners or apothecaries acted as abortionists by introducing a sharp instrument such as a knitting needle into the womb or by giving the patient an abortificant such as lead or pennyroyal. Many cases were fatal due to infection or rupturing of the womb during the procedure. This was a widespread procedure until the legalising of the procedure in 1967.
croncled wrinkled.
croup inflammation of the trachea and larynx (windpipe) common in young children.
If not cured quickly this was a highly fatal disease beginning with a hard dry cough, rapid breathing and hoarseness leading to wheezing and great difficulty in breathing. This was followed by the peculiar crowing, whistling sound of the cough. The disease today is recognised as being caused by a virus.
croupous pneumonia pneumonia which attacks children already suffering from chronic bronchitis or emphysema.
A once common disease in children over 3 years of age, the onset was sudden with a high fever and maybe delirium, rapid pulse, headache, shortness of breath, vomiting, diarrhoea, rasping cough causing severe pain in the side. The tongue would be dry and furry and the breath exceedingly foul. The situation would usually end in gangrene of the lung and the child would be very ill until the 6th–9th day when the fever would abate suddenly and the crisis would be marked by collapse, the child becoming cold and clammy with a subnormal temperature. Death would take place shortly after.
cupping a form of bleeding.
It is performed by blistering the skin with a freshly heated glass cup being applied which causes a vacuum and raises the skin inside. The cup is removed and the inflamed skin is scored with tiny incisions, the

reheated cup is reapplied and blood will steadily flow into the cup.
cyanosis blue discoloration of the extremities.
It occurs wherever the skin is most delicate eg. lips, tip of the nose, eyelids, ears and nails along with mucous membranes of the mouth. It is an indication that the blood is deficient in oxygen and can be caused, in adults, by heart failure some lung diseases or strangulation in which the air is either prevented from reaching the lungs or the lungs cannot function properly. In children it can be caused by the umbilical cord being around the neck during labour and delivery or congenital heart disease.
cynanche old term for severe sore throat and choking (see quinsy).
cystitis inflammation of the bladder due to infection.
If untreated the disease will spread upwards through the ureters to the kidneys.
dancing mania (see St. Vitus dance).
Dandy fever (see dengue).
deafness often caused by childhood diseases such as measles, scarlet fever, chicken pox, meningitis, diphtheria or ear infections.
debility the 1865 definition was weakness or lack of strength, uniform exhaustion of all the organs of the body without specific disease.
When this term is applied to children it could stem from various causes such as a premature birth, a prolonged or difficult birth, congenital abnormality, malnutrition or prolonged disease.

31

degeneration progressive impairement of organs or tissues not necessarily attributed to a specific disease.

degeneratio adiposa et calcarea fatty and calcerous (see atheroma).

dehydration lack or loss of bodily fluid due to excessive sweating during a fever or the inability to swallow due to disease of the digestive tract.

Prolonged dehydration is characterised by sunken eyes, dry mouth, tongue and lips and leads to kidney failure.

delirium rapid onset of confusion, disorient-ation, wild talking or raving or delusions.

It is usually caused by an uncontrolled high temperature or trauma. Patients at this time are irresponsible and have been known to commit suicide.

delirium tremens severe form of delirium caused by withdrawal of alcohol after prolonged alcohol dependency.

The patient is extremely irritable, fretful, nervous and uneasy. Insomnia or nightmares precede the delirium and the patient begins to talk to himself, he is surrounded by frightful animals or is pursued by some one who has designs upon his life. The delirium continues until the patient sinks into a deep sleep from which he awakes comparatively rational or he dies from exhaustion.

delirious mania usually regarded as a violently exaggerated form of acute mania.

Characteristics are excessive and complicated with feverish disturbance. The lips and teeth are dry and crusted and the tongue is covered with a thick brown fur. The pulse and breathing rates are increased and sleeplessness and restlessness are intense. Speech is quite incoherent and the patient may be very noisy. Food is refused, hallucin- ations occur and the condition leads to great exhaustion both bodily and mentally and most cases end fatally. It usually occurs in diseases such as pneumonia or inflammation of the kidneys.

dementia loss or deterioration of memory or reasoning power.

dengue viral infection transmitted to humans by mosquitoes in tropical and sub-tropical regions.

Characterised by swelling and pain in the joints and skin eruptions which are severely itchy. There is a sore throat and runny eyes and the pain in the joints is intense. The symptoms are sudden and short lasting around 3 days but may recur many times over the following months.

dentition teething.

It was once a common cause of death in babies and young children. Babies have no control over their body temperature and prolonged pain and crying would give them a very high fever. They could also suffer from bronchitis, diarrhoea, convulsions or thrush from which they could subsequently die. Babies would also be given rattles, rings or pieces of bone to chew on and their fingers would not always be clean when they sucked them, all of which would lead to infections from which they could die.

derangement insanity.

Derbyshire neck (see goitre).

dermatitis inflammation of the skin due to irritation by any substance to which the skin is sensitive.

Irritant dermatitis is caused when the skin becomes inflamed as a result of contact with a substance. Allergic dermatitis is when the patient becomes hypersensitive or allergic to a substance.

Devonshire colic caused by drinking cider which has been stored in lead containers and the colic occurs as a result of lead poisoning.

Characterised by severe pain in the bowels with distension or flatulence but without looseness or diarrhoea. It would have been very common in Roman times when many of their vessels were made of lead.

diabetes mellitus failure of the pancreas to secrete enough insulin for metabolizing carbohydrates.

It was first recognised as a disease in the 6ᵗʰC. AD when a Hindu physician realised that the symptoms occurred in people who were consuming too much oil and sugar. Until the 1860's it was thought to be a disease of the kidneys due to the large amounts of urine passed by patients and later on it was thought that the liver was producing excess sugar. In 1741 it was described as a frequent and large discharge of pale and sweetish urine attended with constant thirst and a slow wasting of the whole body leading to death.

diaphragm the muscular partition between the chest cavity and the abdominal cavity and is the main muscle used in breathing.

diaphragmatic hernia weakness of the diaphragm which allows the stomach, small intestine or bowel to pass into the chest cavity.

The condition can be congenital or acquired by trauma.

diarrhoea loose or unformed faeces from the bowels. It is a common and important symptom of many intestinal diseases the severity and type varying according to the disease.

When diarrhoea is present and if insuff-icient fluids are taken to replace the loss, dehydration will quickly occur which, in children especially, is fatal. Diarrhoea that kills could also have been due to conditions such as ulcerative colitis or Crohn's disease which even today are serious intestinal diseases, treated by surgical removal of part of the bowel.

dilation of heart (see cardiac dilation).

diphtheria throat infection caused by a bacteria.

This causes inflammation of the throat with the formation of a tough membrane which closes up the throat and causes death by suffocation. Sufferers have a typical swollen 'bull-neck' appearance. A vaccine to prevent infection was discovered in 1913 and in 1940 a national immunisation campaign was launched by the Ministry of Health but not before 45,000 cases and 2,400 deaths had occurred in that year. By 1966 there were only 20 cases of diphtheria in England and Wales which lead to 5 deaths.

diphtheritic paralysis occurs in about 20% of cases of diphtheria.

The bacteria produce a poison capable of damaging nerve tissue thus causing paralysis of various parts of the body Paralysis of the palate is common and the patients voice becomes nasal or 'bleating'. Attempts to swallow result in fluid coming back down the nose. The muscles of the eyes may become paralysed so that the patient is unable to read small print or they will have double vision. If the muscles of speech and swallowing are affected together the condition is very serious as heart attacks are likely to occur as well and, because of the inability to clear the throat by coughing, pneumonia may develop. The most dangerous form of paralysis is that which affects the breathing muscles and the heart, then death is a common result.

disinfectant solution which destroys organisms.

Carbolic acid was first used during surgery by Joseph Lister and later preparations were Lysol and Phenol.

disseminated sclerosis unpredictable, degenerative disease of the central nervous system causing disorder of the optic nerves, brain and spinal cord.

The disease has a very slow onset with temporary paralysis of a limb or an eye muscle causing double vision or tremors of the limbs on exertion. The disease recurs and remits over many years with symptoms ranging from mild to devastating. In the 19ᵗʰC. these conditions were often thought to be hysterical in nature as it was often several years before any other symptoms occurred. Sclerosis is the Greek word for scarring and this occurs on the myelin sheath or protective covering of the nerve fibres causing the nerve communication system to be disrupted. The neurological transmission of messages is slowed down or completely blocked leading to diminished or total loss of all bodily functions which are controlled by the central nervous system such as sight, smell, taste, hearing, touch, movement, speech, thinking, remembering and all reflex actions which happen automatically. Symptoms are many and various including numbness and tingling of the feet and hands, fatigue, fits, blurred vision followed by complete loss, generalised pains, constipation or diarrhoea, incontinence and depression. The temporary paralysis becomes permanent prior to death. The disease usually begins between the ages of 20 to 40 years with no known cause.

distemper ill-health or disease especially an infectious one.

divine sickness (see epilepsy).
So called because many sufferers were thought to be highly intelligent.

dog madness (see rabies).

double pneumonia pneumonia infection affecting both lungs.

dropsy oedema, abnormal collection and water-logging of the tissues by fluid in limbs and cavities of the body.
It is not a disease in itself but due to obstruction of the blood flow through the veins in heart disease; watery condition of the blood allowing fluid to escape through the capillary walls; weakening of the capillary walls due to injury. Heart disease produces increased pressure in the veins and Bright's disease, when the kidneys fail to function properly, are the main causes of general dropsy. A tumour pressing on a large vein in an arm or leg or a thrombosis may cause oedema in the limb. Liver disease may also interfere with the circulation to cause oedema in the abdomen and later in the legs.
The part affected becomes so swollen that the skin loses its natural colour and becomes pale, tense and shining. Pressure

with the finger gives the sensation of kneading a doughy mass and leaves behind a deep depression on the surface. This

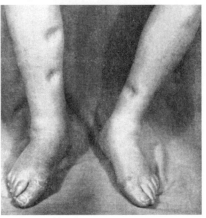

pitting is produced by the fluid being displaced from the tissues and on cessation of the pressure the fluid slowly returns and the pit disappears.

dry belly-ache (see Devonshire colic).

duodenal ulcer occurs in the first part of the small intestine which immediately follows the stomach in the digestive tract.
Together with a gastric or stomach ulcer it is known as a peptic ulcer. Pain in the middle of the upper abdomen occurs 2-3 hours after a meal and can last for up to an hour but is relieved by food or a glass of milk. There are very few signs other than this until the patient loses blood from the bowels making the faeces black and tarry due to the ulcer bleeding or, if the ulcer perforates, immediate surgery is necessary. The perforation allows pus to pour into the abdominal cavity causing peritonitis.

dysentery bacteria in the bowel causing severe diarrhoea.
It is highly infectious and was always present to some extent in the unsanitary overcrowded conditions found in jails, hospitals, camps, slums, etc., but the disease periodically swelled to epidemic proportions when it was invariably fatal.

34

dyspepsia indigestion.

No one would die from this it was probably just a symptom of a more serious disease such as a stomach ulcer or cancer.

dyspnoea difficulty in drawing breath.

eclampsia one of the most serious complications of pregnancy, a severe poisoning of the mothers system occuring in the latter half of pregnancy.

It is characterised by persistant headache, disturbances of vision, flashes of light before the eyes or even temporary blindness, indigestion, high blood pressure, oedema, passing only small amounts of urine and repeated convulsions each one being followed by varying periods of unconsciousness. The fits are recognisable in four stages beginning with twitching of the facial muscles followed by a fixed spasm of the whole body with the jaws tightly clenched and maybe the tongue being bitten. The back is arched and the patient becomes blue. The body then relaxes and begins a stage of alternating spasms and relaxation of all the muscles followed by a coma which may last for a few hours or several days. There may be only one fit or several, and if more than 20 occur, recovery is very unlikely. The term was once also used for infantile convulsions.

ectopic pregnancy (see fallopian tubes).

eczema noncontagious chronic itching inflammatory disease of the skin.

The skin is very red and thickened, with or without oedema, pustules or scaling. It is an intensely unpleasant condition which is triggered by animal hair, food, house dust mite, bacteria or irritants. An impaired barrier function of the skin makes it more susceptible to irritation and the damage from scratching causes further inflammation.

Eczema Capitas is confined to the scalp but a child dying of this condition would probably have infected lesions due to scratching.

edema (see oedema).

effusion the escape of any fluid out of a vessel containing it and its lodgement in another cavity.

Often occurs as an oozing from vessels that have not been ruptured but are diseased.

Elephantiasis Arabum infestation by the filaria worm which lives in the circulatory and lymphatic systems, the connective tissue and serous cavities of its host.

It causes chronic enlargement and thickening of the tissues under the skin. The skin may be rough and lumpy or tight and dry. It is preceded by several attacks of acute inflammation and after each attack the skin is more oedematous. The lower limbs and genitals are most likely to be affected but other parts may occasionally be involved and may weigh several pounds more than normal.

Elephantiasis Graecorum (see leprosy).

emaciated severe wasting, a common symptom of many diseases such as tuberculosis or cancer. Also occurs in diseases of the digestive system when nutrients are not fully absorbed.

embolism the occlusion of a blood vessel by a foreign body.

This could be anything from a blood clot, a tumour, cholesterol or clumps of bacteria.

emphysema lung disease occurring when the partitions between the air cells are broken down and the blood cannot be oxygenated properly. It is caused by an excessive production of an enzyme which dissolves lung tissue.

The breathing in such patients is heavy and noisy, the shoulders are elevated and hunched and the chest is distended although there is very little sputum coughed up. Infections are caught frequently causing permanent inflammation and hardening of the lung tissue which in turn causes loss of elasticity and the inability to inhale a lung full of air.

empiric person who practices medicine relying on experience and experimentation rather than training. (see quack doctor).

empyema collection of pus in any hollow cavity or organ in the body.

The term usually describes pus in the pleural cavities between the lungs and the chest wall and is often a sequel to pneumonia. The onset is sudden with a high fever and symptoms resembling recurring pneumonia. There is cachexia, pallor, anaemia and prostration. There are increased respirations, cough, weight loss and anorexia along with diarrhoea. In chronic cases there may be clubbing of the fingers, albuminurea, swelling of the feet, and often marked lateral curvature of the spine. Empyema may burrow behind the

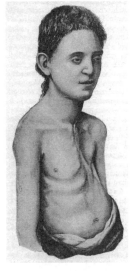

diaphragm into the abdominal cavity and appear as a psoas abscess. Or it may burrow into the lower region of the spine or rupture into the oesophagus or through the diaphragm into the peritoneal cavity. Incision and drainage are the only methods of treatment (as shown above) and mortality is high.

encephalitis inflammation of the brain.

It occurs as a complication of influenza, measles, mumps, scarlet fever, whooping cough or middle ear disease. In rare cases it may follow vaccination. The disease develops suddenly and after one or two days of headache, giddiness, depression or irritability the patient becomes dazed with stiffness of the neck followed by unconsciousness and coma. Death takes place in one or two days. In less acute cases

the fatal end may be delayed for some weeks and paralysis may occur before death.

encephalitis lethargica sleepy sickness, epidemic disease usually occurring in the spring caused by a virus which attacks the cerebellum (the base of the brain) and the brain stem (the section of the brain which leads to the spinal cord).

These areas become oedematous and bleeding with destruction of the tissues and nerve cells. The patient has a fever and becomes increasingly drowsy and lethargic and may progress to a state of complete unconsciousness. As the drowsiness deepens various forms of paralysis occur, the eyelids droop, weakness occurs on one or both sides of the face, the nerves controlling the muscles of the throat are paralysed causing changes in the voice and difficulty swallowing. The effects last for many months and are often fatal. First reported in Eastern Europe in 1916/17.

encephalocele protrusion of a portion of the brain through the skull.

The condition is present at birth as the skull bones are not joined together until the infant is around a year old. It is a similar condition to spina bifida and meningocele but in this case the brain itself protrudes. The deformity is usually accompanied by mental illness and/or paralysis.

endocarditis inflammation of the membrane which lines the cavities and valves of the heart.

endometritis inflammation of the lining of the womb.

English cholera cholera nostrus or summer diarrhoea was common in England long before the more virulent Asiatic cholera arrived. In today's terms it would be classed as food poisoning.

enteric fever typhoid or paratyphoid infection.

Until the early 20^{th}C. it was believed to be spread by emanations from fresh or stale faeces, from the breath or by inhalation of sewer gas from the drains.

enteritis inflammation of the small intestine causing diarrhoea.

enterostomy surgical opening of the abdominal cavity and the bowel to pro-duce a temporary or permanent opening to bypass the remainder of the bowel.

epidemic cholera (see Asiatic cholera).

epidemic encephalitis (see encephalitis lethargica).

epigastric hernia a hernia in the upper part of the abdomen, usually in young men, containing a fatty tumour originating in the lower abdomen.

In the 19^{th}C. this was also classed as a diaphragmatic hernia. Pain occurs after meals and on lying down, haemorrhage and anaemia are also frequently seen.

epilepsy brain disorder characterised by sudden deprivation of all the senses accompanied by violent convulsive fits.

It was once thought to be hereditary or caused by a pregnant mother having a fright. Hippocrates thought that children would be cured when they grew older, moved to a different country or changed their lifestyle.

epistaxis nose bleed.

epithelioma cancer originating in the outermost layer of the mucous membranes and the skin.

Boys who worked as chimney sweeps and were exposed to long continued irritation of the skin by soot were especially vulnerable to this disease.

epulis a tumour growing from the jaws.

A red fleshy mass growing from the gums between and around the teeth which may grow over and almost completely conceal the crowns of the teeth. The teeth are usually bad and pus is present. The condition can be benign or malignant and removal necessitates cutting away the part of the jaw from where the mass arises.

erysipelas a highly contagious streptococcal infection of the skin.

It is frequently seen alongside other debilitating diseases or alcholism. The symptoms appear suddenly with fever, rigors, thirst, vomiting, general malaise and delerium. Between the second and fourth day the area of infection is bright red, swollen and tense and full of small pustules which turn into blisters at which time the fever abates. If erysipelas occurs on the foot the area swells so much that the skin stretches and becomes shiny, there is extreme pain and the swelling may spread up the leg. If the face is affected it swells, becomes red and the area is covered with small pustules filled with clear water. One or both eyes are generally closed with the swelling and there is difficulty in breathing. If the mouth and nostrils are very dry and the patient is drowsy, inflammation of the brain is suspected. If large areas of the body are affected or the red inflammation changes to livid or black it is usually fatal after about seven or eight days.

erythema pernio (see chilblain).

evill, or kings evil, tuberculosis of the lymphatic system.

It is characterised particularly by a swelling of the glands in the neck hence the name scrofula. The Latin scrofa means pig and the swollen neck of the victim gives the face a pig-like expression. It was thought that this disease could be cured by the touch of a king (or queen) and Queen Anne who died in 1714 was the last monarch to practise 'touching'.

excoriation abrasions or chafing of the skin.

It is due to constant irritation of soiled nappies, tight clothing or general lack of cleanliness.

exhaustion loss of mental and physical power due to fatigue, prolonged physical or mental illness, excessive heat or cold.

exopthalmic goitre (see Graves disease).

exostosis a bony benign tumour forming on a bone.

extra dural abscess an abscess forming outside the dura-mater which is the outermost covering of the membranes of the brain just under the skin.

It is usually formed as the result of a scalp wound which does not drain infected pus properly or from a disease of the middle ear which has spread to the brain.

extrinsic allergic alveolitis inflamma-tion of the minute divisions of the glands and air sacs in the lungs caused by an allergic reaction to various substances.

It is characterised by shortness of breath, tightness of the chest, cough and fever and the onset may be sudden or gradual. The patient needs immediate removal from the source of the offending material.

facial paralysis Bell's palsy.

The muscles on one or both sides of the face are paralysed causing inability to close the eye(s) or to smile and show the teeth on the affected side. The mouth is often pulled down to one side. It is caused by damage to the 7th cranial nerve due to inflammation, a wound in front of the ear, a fracture at the base of the skull or a stroke. It may be temporary or permanent.

faeces waste matter excreted from the bowels.

falling of the fundament prolapse of the rectum (bowel) was once quite common among children through weakness of the muscles in that area caused by persistent constipation and straining, diarrhoea or drastic purgatives.

Bladder stones, cystitis, diarrhoea, worms or violent coughing were all thought to bring about a prolapse. The child would be weak and miserable and, depending on the amount of intestine prolapsed, bleeding, mucous discharge and diarrhoea would be present. The irritation and discharge would gradually weaken the child, it would lose weight and become malnourished.

falling disease / sickness (see epilepsy).

fallopian tubes tubes along which female eggs (ova) are transferred from the ovary to the womb (uterus).

If a fertilized egg fails to descend into the womb and continues to grow in the fallopian tube, the tube will eventually rupture and

unless surgically removed can cause peritonitis and death. The patient suffers from excessive and in-cessant vomiting for up to six weeks with increasing severity of abdominal pain. Collapse occurs suddenly as the tube ruptures, anytime up to the fourth month of pregnancy, causing death from shock and/or peritonitis.

false measles (see rubella).

famine fever (see remitting fever).

farcy inflammation of the skin produced by the infectious matter from a horse suffering from farcy.

farmer's lung (see extrinsic allergic alveolitis).

Caused by the inhalation of dust from mouldy hay or straw.

fascioliasis disease caused by a common parasitic worm, the liver fluke, found in sheep and cattle suffering from liver rot.

It is transmitted to humans by means of the Limnoea snails which infect wild unwashed watercress. The patient will suffer from fever, dyspepsia, heavy sweating, loss of appetite, abdominal pain, urticaria and a troublesome cough. In serious cases the disease can cause liver damage. It was once the commonest disease caught in British slaughterhouses.

fatty degeneration of the heart the muscles of the heart degenerate into fat and become incapable of working properly.

favus (see tinea capitas).

febricula simple or little fever of not more than three or four days duration.

felo de se suicide by person of a sound mind and not suffering from any mental instability.

fester a collection of pus in an abscess or ulcer.

fever raised body temperature and rapid pulse caused by disease or infection which if unchecked can lead to delirium.

In the late 18thC. it was thought that fevers were caused by errors in the diet, unwholesome air, violent emotions of the mind, suppression of the usual evacuations

38

(urine and faeces), internal or external injuries and extreme degrees of heat or cold. Fevers are commonly associated with many diseases but can be fatal in children who can not control their own body temperature.

fibrillation non-coordinated twitching of muscle fibres that have been separ-ated from their nerve supply – a term usually used in connection with the heart which results in irregular heartbeats.

fibrinous pneumonia (see croupas pneumonia).

fibroid phthisis chronic type of tuberculosis which has a much slower progression and less bleeding from the lungs than acute tuberculosis.

fibroid pneumonia this should really be called fibrinous pneumonia when nodules of fibrous tissue sometimes as large and as hard as hazelnuts or walnuts are found in the lungs due to inflammation.

fibroid of uterus benign tumour consisting of fibrous tissue growing in the womb not normally life threatening but can cause very heavy bleeding which in turn could lead to anaemia and death.

The first successful operation to remove a uterine fibroid was performed in 1845.

fibrous tissue the inelastic tissue which forms ligaments, and sinews and scar tissue.

fire damp the name given by miners to an explosive mixture of gases including marsh gas (methane) found in mines.

fires in the eye tiny fragments of heated iron or cinders which fly into the eyes.

It is common in occupations such as engine drivers or blacksmiths.

fish kettle (see bronchitis kettle).

fistula unnatural or artificial narrow channel leading from a natural cavity such as a gland or the interior of the bowels to the surface of the skin, or a channel between two cavities where there should be none, as between the bladder and bowel.

They occasionally occur during foetal development but are usually caused by either disease or injury. Most fistulas occur

around the genital area due to trauma often during difficult childbirth. They are usually closed by surgery but the cavity was often packed with dressings to encourage healing from the deepest part, a very painful and laborious undertaking with danger of infection ever present.

fleume (see phlegm).

flux an excessive output of any excretions of the body.

It is usually applied to excretions of the bowel. (see bloody flux).

foetus name given to an unborn child from around 9 weeks after conception through to its birth.

follicular stomatitis (see aphthous stomatitis).

follicular tonsilitis white spots or follicles which develop on the tonsils in the later stages of tonsilitis.

French pockes (see syphilis).

frenzy violent, temporary mental derangement or delirious excitement.

fundament the external opening of the bowel the anus.

gall (see bile).

galling (see excoriation).

galloping consumption acute form of tuberculosis of the lungs.

The patient is suddenly attacked by an intermittent fever with a rapid pulse and rapid loss of strength and flesh. Profuse sweating occurs especially at night and there is pain in the side resembling pneumonia. Early in the attack much blood may be coughed up and within a few days it becomes obvious what the nature of the disease is. As the lung tissue breaks down the spit becomes more abundant, yellow-green in colour with a sickly smell. The patient continues to decline and death occurs within a few weeks.

gall stones hardened deposit in the gall bladder which may move into the bile duct where it becomes impacted and causes severe pain and jaundice.

gangrene necrosis or death of tissues occurs when cells lose their supply of blood and hence their supply of oxygen and nutrients due to disease or injury.

The main artery supplying the area may be torn or crushed as a result of injury, it may be blocked by an embolus, compressed by inflammation or a tumour. There are 2 varieties - dry and moist, the latter being very dangerous, the area is very cold, swollen and discoloured and affords an ideal breeding ground for poisonous organisms and is a serious threat to life. Diabetes and the arterial degeneration of old age often produce gangrene as do burns and frostbite. Gangrene of the internal organs is found in the gut as a consequence of a strangulation or constriction of the blood vessels and in the lungs as a result of infection.

gangrenous carbuncle (see anthrax).

gas gangrene very rapidly spreading form of gangrene common in WWI.

The disease affected wounds, even those of a very trivial nature and caused a very heavy mortality rate. It is caused by a bacteria found in the soil which can only grow in the absence of oxygen. As the bacteria spreads rapidly through the muscles and soft tissues the patient becomes profoundly ill. The activity of the bacteria leads to the formation of gas bubbles in the infected tissues with the result that these become greatly swollen and inflammed, local death occurs and the condition of the patient becomes precarious.

gastric catarrh (see cholera).

gastric fever (see typhoid fever).

gastritis or bilious attack caused by a large indigestible meal, excessive alcohol intake, food poisoning, infections such as influenza or the swallowing of poisons.

The symptoms consist of loss of appetite, nausea or vomiting, headache and giddiness. The tongue is covered with a furry coating, the breath is offensive and there is pain or discomfort in the stomach area.

gastro enteritis inflammation of the stomach and intestines caused by different bacteria including cholera and several types of food poisoning. *Vomiting and diarrhoea are the predominant symptoms and the attack is usually short-lived. However in infants or the elderly, if dehydration is severe, collapse or death can occur.*

gathering an old term for an abscess.

gathering in the throat (see diphtheria)

general paralysis of the insane
It is caused by the effects of syphilis on the brain giving rise to many symptoms both physical and mental leading gradually to increased paralysis of movement and mental ability and usually ending in death within 2-3 years.

Symptoms begin with a decline in mental and physical powers the memory is defective, concentration fails and judgement weakens so that foolish conduct in varying ways may be manifested. The morality of the individual often changes so that excessive drinking and lewd habits occur. A dirty and careless appearance may be in evidence. These symptoms of a general dementia increase along with delusions, hallucinations, slurred speech and confusion. As the patient continues to deteriorate they lose their sense of time, their own identity and all emotions are deadened. They become progressively unable to perform any action requiring intelligence. Tremors of the tongue, hands and lower facial muscles are apparent and the walk becomes ataxic. Epileptic-like fits and muscular twitchings occur and shortly before death there is profound dementia where the patient appears to be a machine more than a person mumbling incoherent sounds. The weakness and tremors are extreme and the ataxia is so severe walking is impossible. Finally exhaustion is extreme the patient is bed-ridden, dirty in their habits and either dies in a state of coma or is quickly carried off by some intercurrent disease.

german measles (see rubella).

giddiness (see vertigo).

gin drinkers liver cirrhosis of the liver which is shrunken with an irregular knobbly surface due to the extensive fibrosis strands which have contracted the organ.

It is usually caused by prolonged excessive intake of alcohol. The general symptoms of cirrhosis include digestive disturbances such as loss of appetite, pain after food, vomiting, diarrhoea, wasting and depression of vitality, fever, jaundice and oedema of the legs. When the condition is well established haemorrhage from the bowel or stomach may occur in fatal quantities. Ascites is a common symptom of advanced cases and is usually followed by death.

glanders an inflammation of the mucous membrane of the nose accompanied by a high fever.

In 1830 it was discovered that this disease could be transmitted from an infected horse to humans. The disease commenced with pain in the abdomen and chest, difficulty in breathing and rigors. The upper half of the face including the eyelids, nose and cheeks would become greatly swollen so that the eyes were closed. The eyelids and cheeks were red, hot, dry and shining but the nose would be dark coloured and maybe black and cold with no feeling in it. There was a thick, deep yellow, blood streaked discharge from the nostrils and several hard pustules around it as well as elsewhere on the body. Around six weeks later swellings would gradually occur all over the body, red at first becoming dark purple. The patient would become progressivly more delirious and agitated with profuse diarrhoea. In an acute attack death usually occurs within 3 weeks and in the chronic form death occurs within 4 months.

gleets ulcers in the urethra producing discharge caused by chronic gonorrhoea.

The main symptoms are mild discharge and discomfort when passing urine and a desire to empty the bladder more frequently. The patient may develop a stricture which will gradually narrow the urethra until the passage of urine is completely stopped. The testicles or bladder may become inflamed and the kidneys damaged due to the backflow from an overful bladder.

gogle a squint.

goitre a swelling on the front of the neck caused by enlargement of the thyroid gland. *This causes much discomfort or exerts great pressure on the windpipe.which in turn*

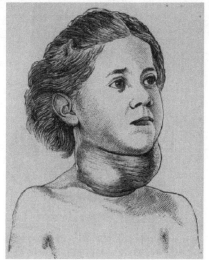

causes difficulty with swallowing and breathing. Common in mountainous limestone areas due to lack of iodine in the drinking water.

gonorrhoea highly infectious, usually sexually transmitted, disease but which can also be caught from towels or clothing which have been used by an infected person. *Symptoms begin with itching and slight pain in the genitals with a watery discharge from the urethra which 'occasions a small degree of titillation particularly in the time of making water'. Gradually the pain and heat of the genitals increases along with inflammation and, in the male, erections become involuntary and very painful and the testicles are swollen. Swellings in the groin*

41

appear, urine is passed with great difficulty or suppressed altogether. Inflammation of the joints leads to permanent stiffness and occasionally blood poisoning leads to inflammation of the heart valves and abscesses in various parts of the body. In females the disease attacks the reproductive system causing sterility or peritonitis. In 1964 there were 37,665 new cases of gonorrhoea attending clinics in England and Wales for treatment.

gossips a group of women invited to assist the midwife during labour and childbirth.

This word is a corruption of the Old English god-sib or god-sibling the source of today's godparent. In the 16th C. it was someone invited to witness the birth for the purpose of later providing proof, at the baptism, that the child had not been born dead and another surreptitiously exchanged in its place. The group usually consisted of five or six close friends and relatives including the mother of the labouring woman.

gout a metabolic inbalance of uric acid which causes recurrent attacks of severe painful swellings in joints affecting all joints especially the great toe.

The swellings caused are called tophi and contain a soft cheesy substance and often ulcerate. If injured the tophi can become infected leading to generalised septicaemia.

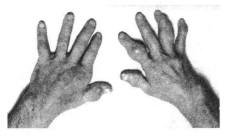

The peculiar pain of gout is likened to the feeling of a dog gnawing at the bones. It was always thought to be caused by rich living – too much wine and rich food.

gouty synovitis term used when some internal organs become affected with gout.

granular kidneys also called gouty kidney as the condition is found usually in conjunction with gouty arthritis.

The kidneys shrivel and contain crystals of sodium due to the high concentration of salt in the bloodstream.

gravell kidney or bladder stones.

They were said to be caused by high living, the use of strong astringent wines and a sedentary life. Prior to the mid 17th C.. approximately 1 in 12 of the English aristocracy, including Samuel Pepys, endured the anguish of the stone or its removal without anaesthetic.

Grave's disease abnormal functioning of the thyroid gland producing too much thyroid.

The patient's eyes seem to be bulging out of the head as the eyeball is thrust forward and the whites of the eyes gleam in a most alarming fashion. The whole attitude of the body is one of anxiety with a very fine tremor of the muscles and increased heart rate. The skin is flushed and the patient is always warm. The thyroid gland in the neck is enlarged and the patient suffers from alternating nervous excitement and depression.

grease or equinia mitis a pustular eruption of the skin produced by the infectious matter from a horse affected with the grease.

green sickness a form of mild anaemia once common among young women.

grinder's asthma or 'grinders rot', silicosis, a common lung disease among the knife grinders of Sheffield and the needle-makers of Worcestershire and also found among coal hewers, flax and feather dressers, workmen in millstone quarries and stone-masons.

Grinders who have good constitutions seldom experience much inconvenience from their trade till they arrive at about 20 years of age. Symptoms then begin to steal upon them, breathing becomes difficult on exertion and their shoulders become elevated to relieve their constant and *increasing shortness of breath. Their complexions assume a dirty muddy appearance and their countenance indicates anxiety. There is tightness in the chest and their voice is rough and hoarse. Their cough is loud as if air is being driven through wooden tubes and they occasionally cough up considerable quantities of dust in hard lumps. This is sometimes mixed with mucus, sometimes frothy and in more advanced stages copious and purulent. The mucus is sometimes dusky red and frequently fresh blood is coughed up. Many grinders affected did not live to see their 50thbirthday* .(see also pneumoconiosis).

gripes green sour smelling diarrhoea and abdominal pain usually occurring in children who have been fed incorrectly.

grocer's itch (see baker's itch).

growth term usually applied to a cancerous tumour.

gruel watery drink for invalids made from 2 ounces of oatmeal boiled with 2 pints of water with either sugar or salt added.

gum rash urticaria or nettle rash in babies.
Usually affects children under 2 years of age and is frequently associated with indigestion or constipation. The rash consists of pink blotches with a red centre slighly raised above the skin. Blebs may occur making the condition appear to be chicken pox. The blotches appear at night and fade during the day and the irritation caused leads to scratching which introduces an infection into the skin.

gumma syphilitic ulcers.
They occur in patients who have been infected with the disease for over 2 years. They may be anything from the size of a melon seed up to the size of a hen's egg and several may be present at any one time. They occur anywhere in the body and if they are just under the skin cause very extensive ulcers. On the tongue they are often mistaken for cancer and in the mouth cause widespread destruction of the bones of the face and nose. In the liver they cause

extensive damage but the most dangerous occurrence is in the brain where they induce paralysis, blindness, coma and death.

haemolytic disease of the newborn (see icterus neonatorum).

haematuria blood in the urine caused by bladder or kidney disease.

haemoptysis bleeding from the lungs. *Coughing up blood-streaked sputum usually seen in cases of tuberculosis.*

haemorrhage leakage of blood from vessels, can be either internal or external.

haematemesis vomiting blood.
It is commonly caused by a stomach ulcer or cancer and the dark coloured vomit resembles coffee grounds.

hame old term for skin.

hare lip and cleft palate incomplete fusion of the upper lip and failure of the palate (the roof of the mouth) to close separating the mouth from the nasal cavities.
In the late 1800's it was said to be caused by frights or shocks to the mother while she was pregnant.
There are varying degrees of deformity and a hare lip can occur without a cleft palate or vice versa. The lack of a firm upper palate means 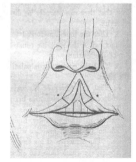 *that the child cannot create a vaccuum in the mouth when sucking and milk comes down the nose before the child can swallow it. A special rubber teat was designed which had a large flap on the upper side which acted as a partial seal and enabled the child to suck properly. The only solution is surgical but many children died either before or after the operation as they were very malnourished.*

harvest mite particularly prevalent in the turf of the south downs and in newly

43

harvested corn and oat fields of the southern counties of England.

The larvae are found in grass, gooseberry bushes and other vegetation. The mites are about one thirtieth of an inch long and reddish in colour from whence they acquired the popular name of 'bete rouge'. The mite invades 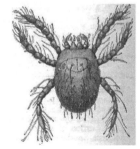 *the human skin particularly of the legs and arms and causes great irritation.*

heare hair.

heart attack blockage of the blood supply to the heart leading to death of part of the heart muscle.

The fatty build up or plaques occurring in atherosclerosis can break open and lead to the formation of a blood clot that seals the break but reduces the blood flow. If a blood clot suddenly cuts off most or all of the blood supply to the heart the cells in the heart muscle do not receive enough oxygen and begin to die. A heart attack begins with discomfort, pressure, squeezing, fullness or pain in the chest, pain in one or both arms, back, neck, jaw or stomach. There is shortness of breath, a cold sweat, nausea or lightheadedness. If the blood supply is not restored within 20-30 minutes irreversible death of the heart muscle will occur. Muscle can continue to die for 6-8 hours after the onset of the attack and the dead muscle is replaced by scar tissue which will not function as efficiently ever again.

heart disease general non-specific term for any number of diseases which may affect the heart.

heart failure when the heart is no longer able to pump hard enough to circulate blood around the body.

It is due to either disease or old age.

heart madness (see auricular fibrillation).

heat cramps painful cramp in the muscles of men employed as furnacemen.

The hot working conditions cause excessive sweating and the cramp is caused by loss of salt in the tissues.

heat stroke heat hyperpyrexia occurs from exposure to excessive heat from the sun or overheated air.

It is characterised by a body temperature of above 40.5 degrees centigrade (normal 37 degrees centigrade). The effects of this on the central nervous system produce convulsions and unconcsiousness and leads to death if the temperature is not stabilised.

hemiplegia paralysis of one side of the body usually due to a stroke.

hepatitis inflammation of the liver.

This is caused by several viruses, A,B,C,D, and E. Hepatitis B virus causes the most serious liver damage and the virus can remain infective for over a week in a drop of dried blood. It is a hundred times more infectious than HIV and causes 80% of liver cancers worldwide. The virus is caught from any contact with blood from an infected person.

hepititis icterus jaundice caused by inflammation of the liver.

hernia the protrusion of an organ, usually the bowel, through the containing wall of its cavity.

An inguinal hernia occurs in the vicinity of the groin, a femoral hernia occurs near the thigh, a scrotal hernia is where the bowel descends into the scrotum, and umbilical hernia occurs near the umbilicus (navel/belly button).

hiatus hernia (see epigastric hernia).

hiccup a succession of spasmodic contractions of the diaphragm which in 1781 was recognised as the forerunner of death in any serious illness.

hicket hiccough or hiccup.

hives (see urticaria).

hoarseness harsh grating voice caused by disease of the throat or larynx (windpipe).

hob nail liver (see gin drinkers liver).
Hodgkin's disease (see lymphadenoma)
honey scab (see impetigo).
honey sickness (see impetigo).
hookworm disease (see ankylomiasis).
hooping cough (see whooping cough).
horn-pox (see modified smallpox).
housemaid's knee (see bursitis).
Huntington's chorea forceful, jerky, rapid, involuntary movements of the muscles caused by a disorder of the central nervous system.
It is usually inherited with an onset in later life between the ages of 30-40 years and if not controlled by sedatives patients will die from exhaustion 5-15 years after the onset of the symptoms.
hydrocephalus obstruction of the flow of spinal fluid in the brain preventing its proper absorption.
It occurs in babies before the bones of the skull are united. The brain is distended and the skull expanded by an abnormal collection of cerebro-spinal fluid. The child

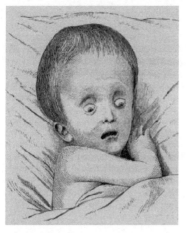

has a large head out of all proportion to the rest of the body and the forehead is prominent.
hydrophobia extreme fear of water (see rabies).
hydrops ascites (see dropsy).

hydrops foetalis usually stillborn child due to rhesus incompatibility with the mother (see icterus neonatorum).
hydrothorax fluid in the chest cavity caused by pleurisy or pneumonia.
hyperdilation of the heart enlargement and thickening of one or more of the cavities of the heart occurring as a consequence of high blood pressure and valvular disease of the heart.
hyperemesis gravidarium excessive vomiting during pregnancy whereby the mother becomes starved of nourishment.
In extreme cases termination of pregnancy is performed to preserve the mother's life.
hyperpieses extremely high blood pressure.
hyperpyrexia uncontrolled extremely high temperature.
hypertension prolonged high blood pressure which if untreated can damage the heart, brain, eyes and kidneys.
In some cases there is no cause found for high blood pressure in others it is due to kidney disease, certain hormone diseases, narrowing of the aorta, ageing or induced by certain drugs eg. the oral contraceptive pill. The measurement of blood pressure is by a machine. (see sphygmomanometer).
hypertrophy an increase in the size of an organ which is due to enlargement of its cells and not due to natural growth.
hypostatic pneumonia (see basal pneumonia).
hypothermia sub-normal body temperature.
Children and the elderly are particularly susceptible to prolonged periods of cold which can lead to death.
hysterectomy surgical operation to remove the female womb (uterus).
hysteria one of the most curious and distressing of feminine maladies.
It is a usual outcome of a failure to direct the mental faculties in proper channels, or of unhealthy excitement and excess. A woman is more prone to it at the extremes of her sexual life, either while she is yet in her teens or at the change of life. It is a most

unpleasant sight to see a person in a fit of hysteria. It comes on with a feeling of choking, as if a ball were in the throat. The patient quickly passes into a state of great excitement, alternately laughing and crying, partly unconscious and wildly incoherent. She is, for a while better after the fit or until the time is ripe for another attack, and this is determined greatly by her surroundings.

hysterical epilepsy common in children where an attack of hysteria alternates with an epileptic fit.

The symptoms are many and varied, the child may start barking like a dog or mewing like a cat or may attempt to bite their carers. The head may be banged about and the legs and arms thrown widely about as if the child were directing the movements. However the child is unconscious during the attack and will have no memory of it afterwards. A sharp word or pin prick will stop the attack.

hysterick cholick is attended with a violent pain about the pit of the stomach with great sinking of spirits and often with greenish vomitings.

icterus neonatorum jaundice (yellowness) of the skin occurring a few days after birth.

The main cause is when the mother becomes sensitized to her unborn child and passes antibodies through the placenta to the foetus which destroys its red blood cells if she is rhesus negative and the child is rhesus positive. The child if born alive will be severely anaemic and probably have oedema in the chest and abdominal cavities. The only treatment is the immediate exchange of blood at birth or prior to delivery.

ictus old term for a stroke.

ileum lower section of the small intestine leading to the jejynum.

iliac passion (see enteritis).

imbecile severe mental retardation.

immaturity (see premature birth).

imperforate anus abnormal closure of the anal opening before birth.

Also, it was once called imperfect bowel.

impetigo common highly infectious skin disease caused by bacteria affecting people of all ages but mainly children and adolescents.

The disease begins as one or more transient reddish patches of skin usually on the face. The horny outer layer of these patches is then raised up into a blister filled with clear fluid. The fluid rapidly becomes thick and as the blisters rupture they discharge a characteristic sticky or gummy substance which dries quickly and forms honey or amber coloured crusts. The crusts are surrounded by a rose coloured ring and from under them there is a constant flow of the sticky discharge. The condition is easily spread on bedding and towels.

impetigo neonatorum a highly infectious form of bullous impetigo.

The disease occurs between the 4th and 10th day of life and severe complications such as nephritis, pneumonia, lung abscess and meningitis may prove fatal even in treated cases. The condition is a serious problem in institutions such as hospitals or nurseries where the infection can be spread easily by nurses or doctors. (see bullous impetigo).

imposthume abscess.

inanition exhaustion from want of food.

The term is usually applied to infants whose mother has little or no breast milk with which to feed the child.

incarceration/acute obstruction abnormal imprisonment of some types of hernia which is impossible to put back in place. If the bowel is involved it becomes obstructed (see obstruction of bowel).

incontinence of urine the inability to hold urine in the bladder for any length of time.

Coughing, laughing etc., will cause dribbling of urine even when the bladder has been recently emptied. Can be caused by prolapse of the womb and lax pelvic muscles in women or by prostate tumours in men.

indigestion (see dyspepsia).

46

infantile convulsions (see convulsions).
They are due to infection, malnutrition, worms, teething, congenital deformity, hydrocephalus.
infantile paralysis (see polio).
infection the process by which a disease is communicated from one person to another.
By direct contact with a sick person; airborne, waterborne or in dust; from a healthy person who is a carrier of an organism without being ill themselves; flies, fleas, ticks, mosquitoes.
infective pyelitis inflammation of the pelvis (the basin shaped edge) of the kidney due to an infection.
inflammation caused by infection, viruses or injury and characterised by redness, swelling, heat, pain and impairment or loss of function of the affected part.
inflammation of the brain (see meningitis).
influenza epidemic infection occurs annually in winter spread by coughing, sneezing, talking or on contaminated hands.
This was once thought to be caused by hostile planets or comets and was called the English sweat, posting sweat, stop gallant or epidemic catarrhal fever due to its rapid onset. The gentry dancing at the court at 9pm could be dead by 11pm and even today influenza is fatal in the elderly as complications include chest infections or pneumonia. Symptoms of extreme fatigue, weakness, aches and pains, headaches, aching eyes, fever, cough and nasal obstruction are common either individually or all together. In 1918 an epidemic caused 50 million deaths worldwide, 250,000 of those were in the UK in a 4 week period. The disease appeared suddenly and victims rapidly became very red in the face, almost purple, had severe nosebleeds and dropped down dead, drowning in their own body fluids.
inguinal hernia hernia of the lower bowel protruding into the groin.

inocculation the deliberate infection of a person by rubbing material from a smallpox pustule into a scratch on the arm.
The recipient would develop smallpox but because the infection did not take place by the normal route a particularly mild form developed, which stimulated the body's own immune system to produce antibodies against further infection. The practice has been used in India and China for many centuries but was brought to England in 1721 by Lady Mary Wortley whose husband was ambassador to the Ottoman Empire. Edward Jenner discovered the far safer cowpox vaccine in 1798.
insular sclerosis (see disseminated sclerosis).
intermitting fever (see ague).
intestinal catarrh sometimes called summer diarrhoea and common among children.
The symptoms begin with vomiting, diarrhoea, fever, restlessness, irritability. The abdomen is distended with wind and the legs drawn up because of the pain. Mucus and bile are vomited and the faeces are watery and full of undigested food, frothy and either yellow or green. The tongue becomes coated with a thick white fur, thirst is extreme but with immediate vomiting afterwards. Faeces are passed every few minutes causing inflamed skin around the napkin area. As the illness progresses the eyes become sunken and kept partly closed the face is pale and the muscles lose their tone causing the head to loll about. The infant then becomes generally listless, the vomiting and diarrhoea cease, stomatitis appears along with convulsions and the child falls into a coma and expires rapidly.
interstitial nephritis inflammation of the tubules in the kidney caused by disease.
intestinal fever (see typhoid fever).
intestinal obstruction (see intussusception).
It is possibly also due to a tumour or chronic constipation.

47

intussusception the folding of one part of the intestine inside itself like a telescope causing an obstruction.

The patient begins vomiting and has constipation and symptoms of severe shock, marked prostration, pallor with an anxious expression on the face. The hands and feet become cold and there is cold perspiration. At the beginning of the disease the temperature is usually subnormal and if it rises rapidly is usually a sign of impending death within 24 hours. Most cases die within 7 days from peritonitis and shock. This was a common condition in children under the age of 12 years and without surgery death was inevitable.

ischemia diminished supply of blood to an organ or area due to a blockage or narrowing of the arteries.

itch mite (see scabies).

jail fever (see typhus).

jaundice yellowness of the skin, mucous membranes and urine, due to liver disease.

jejunum a section of the small intestine leading from the ileum to the large intestine.

Jesuit's bark (see peruvian bark).

It was so called when it was brought to Europe from the West Indies by the Romish missionaries.

jungle fever (see ague).

king's evil (see scrofula).

kybbes chilblains.

la grippe French term for influenza.

It is said to have been applied to an outbreak with pneumonia like symptoms in 1803.

lardaceous disease (see amyloid disease).

laryngismus stridulus spasm of the muscles closing the glottis producing a strident sound which can be mistaken for croup.

The attack comes on suddenly and the child throws back its head, the face becomes pale then livid and for a time there is complete cessation of respiration. This continues for a few moments during which the cyanosis deepens and the child seems in great distress making violent efforts to breathe If the attack is a severe one it may lead to loss of consciousness and may be fatal or the attack may terminate in convulsions. The condition today is known as breath holding and is rare after the age of 2 years.

laryngitis inflammation of the larynx or upper part of the windpipe causing loss of voice.

In severe cases the large amount of swelling could cause suffocation.

lateral sclerosis degenerative disease of the nervous system resulting in weakness and spasticity of the limbs.

laudanum was the base ingredient of soothing syrup.

It was invented in the $16^{th}C$. by the Swiss alchemist and physician Paracelsus (1493-1541) and was made from a mixture of opium dissolved in alcohol. At the height of its popularity, in the mid $19^{th}C$., it is estimated that 15,000 children died each year through overdosing, that was more than died from starvation.

lead palsy paralysis of the forearms due to lead poisoning.

It was common among workers in white lead factories, painters, plumbers, pottery glazers using oxide of lead and bleachers of Brissels lace. The patient suffers general ill health with a sallow complexion and complains of a metallic taste in the mouth. Colic and vomiting are common and a blue line forms along the edges of the gums next to the teeth. The paralysis affects particular muscles so that the patient cannot extend the back of the hand and the wrist drops and cannot be raised. The affected muscles become wasted and a hollow appears in the back of the forearm. Occasionally muscles of the shoulders and back are also affected.

lepra (see leprosy).

leprosy an infectious skin disease which slowly spreads to involve soft tissue and bone causing deformity.

The disease begins with small pimples appearing on the arms, legs and thighs.

These slowly increase in size and spread to the face causing much disfigurement as they are round, hard and varying from the size of a pin head to a pea. The spots begin to cover the forehead, cheeks, chin, nose and ears and some become soft. If they are punctured a clear fluid escapes. The eyelids are thickened and knobbly and the eyebrow hair falls out. The eyes are runny and the voice very husky. Crusts of dark grey or brown appear which if removed reveal an ulcer underneath. The skin feels very thick

and the palms of the hands and soles of the feet are very dry. The toenails become very horny and there is numbness of the feet and hands and loss of sensation. The skin eventually becomes discoloured and ulcers appear in the mouth, the tongue becomes dry and cracked as the patient is unable to swallow. Blebs form on the site of the old ulcer scabs, there is general soreness over the surface of the body, the breath is extremely offensive and breathing difficult. Delirium and great prostration precede death but the process can take between 2-3 years. It is now treatable with antibiotics if discovered in the early stages. It is thought that some references to leprosy may in fact have been pellagra as the two diseases have a superficial resemblance. In medieval England the church and the medical profession forbade carnal relations between a man and a menstruating woman as they maintained that the result would be a child suffering from leprosy.

leprye (see leprosy).

leptospirosis a disease caused by the microorganism Leptospira which is normally found in rodents and small mammals but can be aquired by humans from contaminated water.

Farmers, sewage and abatoir workers, fish cutters and veterinary surgeons are particularly at risk but it can also be caught by swimming in rivers and lakes. The diseaase varies in intensity from mild influenza-like symptoms to a fatal form of jaundice due to severe liver disease. The kidneys may be affected and it can also cause meningitis.

lesion structural or functional alteration of soft tissue or bone due to disease.

lethargy mental or physical drowsiness.

It could be caused by illness or deficiency in the diet.

leucocythaemia abnormal increase in white blood cells, known today as leukaemia or cancer of the blood stream. It *causes enlargement of the spleen and lymph glands throughout the body.*

levant fever (see brucellosis).

lice (see pediculus).

lienteric diarrhoea a form of diarrhoea which is directly related to taking food.

It is a type of nervous diarrhoea and the sensitiveness of the intestines is greatly increased and the bowels may be opened 2-3 times after every meal. However the general condition of the patient usually remains good.

liverish sensation sometimes spoken of as an attack of the blues.

It consists of a group of symptoms that are unpleasant but not of sufficient severity to make the patient take to his bed. Depression, irritability and wandering of attention are accompanied by dull headache, drowsiness and insomnia. The skin looks sallow, the eyes are dull and the tongue slightly furred. The appetite is lost and food causes nausea and pain in the upper abdomen. It is most usually found in persons of middle age living in towns and sedentary workers. It is caused by over taxing the function of the liver due to excess food or alcohol or to an accumulation of waste products in the bowels.

lobar pneumonia (see croupas pneumonia).

lockjaw (see tetanus).

locomotor ataxy (see ataxy).

longe lung.

Ludwig's angina severe inflammation and swelling of the neck.

It is caused by bacteria in the mouth or around the tonsils, which is normally harmless. If through abrasions they pass into the cellular tissue of the neck the patient is in grave danger of choking due to the swelling or suffers from severe blood poisoning.

lues old term for syphilis.

lunatic person who is mentally ill.

The Mental Treatment Act of 1930 rendered this term obsolete.

lunatic asylum see asylum.

lupus erythematosus until the mid 20[th]C. this disease was thought to be a local reaction of the skin to a variety of organisms. It is now known to be a chronic disease of the immune system which instead of protecting the body against disease forms antibodies that attack healthy tissues and organs.

It appears in various forms frequently in middle age. It usually begins with a small, hard, red spot covered with a hard chalk like, friable covering but which is an exceedingly adherent scale. When removed its under surface is seen to be covered with minute spines. The adjacent patch of skin is very red and as the rash spreads the centre heals leaving red edges. A second variety has nodules with persistent reddening and thickening but no scales. The most usual sites for the development of the disease are the nose, cheeks, ears, scalp and backs of the fingers and when the nose and cheeks are involved an area looking like a butterfly appears giving rise to the name 'Butterfly lupus'. When it occurs on the scalp the hair

follicles are destroyed leaving permanent patches of baldness. The disease is now known to affect also the joints, kidneys, heart, lungs, blood, nervous system and other body organs as well as the skin and can be life threatening.

lupus vulgaris tuberculosis of the skin which develops very slowly and causes scarring, usually occurs on the face.

The lesion is very distinctive like 'apple jelly' and sometimes as large as a pea. Fresh lesions appear in the neighbour-hood of the original and as they increase in size they merge together. By now the patch is slightly raised above the skin and the centre of the affected area resolves leaving a scar. The scar is never sound however and relapsing nodules can always be found. Infection is common and sepsis occurs with the area covered with crusts, scabs and pustules. One of the chief sites of the disease is the nose from where it will spread to the palate as well as the cheeks. It rarely attacks bone but the nasal cartilages are often destroyed.

lusk (see dysentery).

lying in labour, childbirth and the following 4 weeks.

Mothers were encouraged to stay in bed or in the lying-in room for up to four weeks after delivery.

lymphadenoma or Hodgkin's Disease a malignant disease of the lymphatic system.

First described by Thomas Hodgkin (1798-1866) a pathologist at Guy's Hospital, London. The glands of the lymphatic system gradually undergo great enlargement. The patient suffers a fever which subsides then reoccurs frequently along with debilitating anaemia.

lymphatic system a mesh of very fine delicate chanels carrying lymph which is a colourless watery fluid.

The lymphatic system circulates throughout the body in a similar way to the blood supply carrying lymph from all parts of the body to the nearest lymph glands. Lymphatic vessels readily take up septic and waste material and convey it to the glands which act as filters and serve to prevent bacteria from entering the general circulation.

lyssa (see rabies).

macule small discoloured spot on the skin which is not raised above the surrounding area.

maidism (see pellagra).

malaria Italian word for 'bad air' (see ague)

malignant disease or growth which spreads rapidly and is usually fatal if not removed.

The term is mainly used today for cancer but was once used to describe any severe disease.

malignant cholera (see asiatic cholera).

malignant fever (see typhus).

malignant hypertension rare condition.

It is characterized by extremely high blood pressure, blood in the urine, kidney failure and damage to the light receptive area of the eyes. Unlike ordinary hypertension which has no symptoms patients with malignant hypertension will suffer from dizziness, angina, breathlessness, visual deterioration. Unless treated the condition is always fatal and death occurs from heart or kidney failure or stroke.

malignant pustule (see anthrax).

malignant quinsy highly infectious throat disease more common in the south of England.

There are symptoms of shivering and fever and extreme weakness when the patient is apt to faint when sitting up. The eyes become red and there is dimness of sight, nausea, vomiting and diarrhoea and the face swells. The throat is very swollen and bright red with white ulcers covering the tonsils. A rash appears on the neck, arms, breast and fingers about the 2nd or 3rd day and there is often slight delirium. The face appears bloated, the nostrils are red and inflamed and the patient complains of a disagreable putrid taste and the breath is very offensive. If the patient is very weak, with frequent shiverings and the nose begins to bleed the outcome is usually fatal.

malignant scarlet fever a gangrenous condition of the throat resembling diphtheria.

There is much swelling of the neck but often no rash. Enlarged infected tonsils accompany a high temperature, diarrhoea, restlessness, with the neck being hard and tense to the touch. The skin is a dull lurid colour and the hands and feet are cold and there is much nasal discharge and foul secretion from the tonsils. The majority of cases die between the 4th and 7th day but if life is prolonged pneumonia occurrs prior to death.

malta fever (see brucellosis).

mammary abscess breast abscess.

It usually occurs during the first few weeks of breast feeding when an infection enters the breast from a cracked nipple or lack of hygene. The breast will be red, swollen, hard and extremely painful when the baby sucks. Prior to the use of antibiotics the mother would become feverish and the baby was often weaned early, fed by a wet nurse or became malnourished and died.

mania obsession, compulsion or abnormal preoccupation.

marasmus severe wasting of the tissues.

It causes wrinkled, inelastic skin, loss of muscle tissue and body fat leading to growth failure, lethargy, extreme exhaustion, sloughing of the skin, necrosis of the bone and death. It is mostly seen in children due

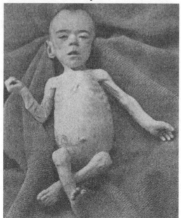

to malnutrition or the inability of the body to absorb nutrients from a good food supply.

marsh fever (see ague).

mastoiditis inflammation of the mastoid cells in the inner ear near the temporal bone of the skull.

If an abscess occurs in this area and ruptures it may cause meningitis or thrombosis and if untreated can slowly spread to the brain causing death.

match worker's disease (see phossy jaw).

maw worms (see roundworms).

measles infectious childhood disease.

Symptoms begin with all the appearances of a severe cold, the child sneezes, has alternating fits of heat and cold, sickness and loss of appetite, the tongue is white but moist and there a cough. There then follows a heaviness of the head and eyes, drowsiness and a runny nose. In severe cases the eyes become inflammed and discharging and acuteness of sensation so that any bright light is painful. The eyelids often swell causing temporary blindness but severe cases cause permanent blindness. Sore throat, vomiting and green diarrhoea often precede the rash and nose bleeds are common. About the 4th day small spots resembling flea bites appear, first upon the face, then the chest then the arms and legs.

About the 6th or 7th day the spots begin to fade and are gone by the 9th day. The fever and difficulty in breathing however often continues. A child suffering from a violent diarrhoea prior to the appearance of measles is in very grave danger and those that die from the disease generally do so around the 9th day from peripneumony or inflammation of the lungs. Rhazes a 10thC. Arabian physician wrote a treatise on the disease but it was often confused with smallpox and scarlet fever. There were epidemics of measles in London in 1670 and 1674. The discovery of vaccination in 1964 drastically reduced the death rate from this disease.

mediastinum the structures in the middle of the chest between the lungs.

mediterranean fever (see brucellosis).

meigrim migrain.

melanoma tumour arising from a darkly pigmented mole on the skin.

These tumours are usually malignant and are the fastest growing of all cancers.

melancholia/melancholy severe depression with suicidal tendencies.

It was unrecognised as a true mental illness until the 16thC. but Hippocrates wrote that if fear and sorrow are present for a long period it denotes the approach of melancholy.

member the penis.

It was also known as a Yard.

membranous croup (see diphtheria).

meninges three membranes covering the brain and spinal cord, the pia mater, dura mater and arachnoid mater.

meningitis inflammation of the membranes covering the brain (cerebral meningitis) or the spinal cord (spinal meningitis).

It is caused by several infectious organisms but could be tubercular, pneumococcal, pyogenic, syphilitic or meningococcal meningitis. The fluid around the membranes and the spinal cord increases with the infection and the pressure causes irritation resulting in headache, vomiting, photophobia (aversion to bright light), stiff neck, convulsions, paralysis and coma. All types of meningitis were fatal until the discovery of anitibiotics. Although it is a relatively rare disease today due to childhood vaccination introduced in 1996, there were 1,985 cases notified in 1974.

meningocele protrusion of the membranes, that cover the brain, through a defect in the skull.

Repeated removal of the fluid is sometimes performed but the deformity is often accompanied by idiocy or paralysis and the child usually dies.

meningococcal meningitis a dangerous epidemic disease affecting the coverings of the brain – the meninges.

It was first recognised in 1837 when it swept through troops in south west France. In 1846 there was an epidemic in the workhouses of Belfast and Dublin and in 1907-1909 large areas of Scotland suffered. Outbreaks usually occur in the early months of the year – February, March and April and the onset is very sudden and the incubation period is only 3-5 days. Patients may be perfectly well one minute and fall down suddenly in a convulsion or go to bed at night with no symptoms and be found unconscious the next morning. Red spots appear all over the trunk and death occurs often suddenly from heart failure within a week of the onset of symptoms.

menorrhagia excessive bleeding from the womb.

It can be caused by fibroids, endometritis or cancer.

mental excitation exciting or stress factors in a person suffering from a mental illness which increases the risk of mental breakdown.

Causes include defective nutrition, infectious diseases, diseases of the blood and circulation, the effects of alcohol or drugs. Life crisis such as adolescence, childbirth, menopause etc., can also provoke extra mental stress.

mercury a lustrous, bluish-white, heavy liquid metal from which the salts have been extracted and used in medicine for many centuries.

It is a highly poisonous substance used as a disinfectant and antiseptic for skin diseases or internally as a purgative. It was the chief remedy for syphillis until the 20^{th}C. An overdose resulted in nausea, vomiting, faintness, impaired balance and severe pain in the throat and chest. There was violent diarrhoea, cramps and supression of urine while the lips, tongue and throat became so swollen that swallowing was impossible. After several hours the breath became very offensive, saliva poured from the mouth and ulcers appeared on the inside of the mouth and tongue. The gums became spongy as life gradually ebbed away.

mesenteric disease the mesentery is a large fold of the peritoneum to which are attached the small intestines. It can be subject to diseases such as cancer, necrosis of the tissue due to inadequate blood supply or twisting of the intestines.

metastasis cancer which has spread from the primary tumour to another part of the body.

metritis inflammation of the womb.

It often occurred after childbirth due to infection. (see childbed fever).

miasma unhealthy vapours in the air thought to cause disease.

middle ear disease infection of the section of the ear behind the tympanic membrane (ear drum).

It is caused by many infections including measles and scarlet fever or by perforating the ear drum with a foreign body. The middle ear connects with the upper respiratory tract via the tympanic tube causing infection to spread from one to the other very easily. There is intense throbbing or a sharp pain accompanied by a high temperature and deafness. The ear drum is bright red or may be perforated due to the build up of pus behind it. If untreated it can lead to mastoiditis, intercranial sepsis, septecaemia, permanent deafness, cerebral asbcess, meningitis or death. Chronic

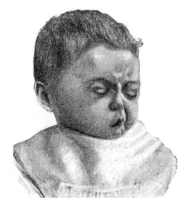

infection could be due to tuberculosis infection and occasionally paralysis of the face can occur. It is mainly caused by a streptococcal infection and was common a hundred years ago due to poor nutrition and housing. The disease today is treatable with antibiotics.

miliary fever took its name from the small pustules which appeared on the skin the same shape and size as seeds of millet.

It is described as a symptom of other diseases such as smallpox, measles or nervous fever but could occur alone. It was

more common in women than men and in persons who were delicate, indolent, kept continually within doors and lived upon a weak watery diet. Women of this type were extremely likely to be seized with the disease in childbed when it was usually fatal. Symptoms began with slight shivering which was succeeded by fever, loss of strength, faintness, sighing, difficulty breathing, and anxiety. The patient was restless, delirious, the tongue was white, the hands shook and the palms were very hot. There was an itching and prickling under the skin before the pustules appeared but then the symptoms began to disappear. About the 6th or 7th day the pustules began to dry and fall off which caused intense itching.

miliary tuberculosis an acute form of tuberculosis following on from chronic tuberculosis of the glands or bones but often a sequel to an attack of measles, whooping cough or typhoid.

Minute nodules or tubercles are formed in several organs of the body as the bacteria is spread via the blood stream.

miliary tuberole tubercles of the same size spread uniformly throughout a diseased organ.

In 1869 this was referred to as tubercular meningitis.

milk crust (see tinea capitas).

milk fever inflammation of the breasts shortly after childbirth giving rise to hard red, tender breasts and fever.

In the days before asepsis and antibiotics almost every lying in woman had a fever on the 3rd or 4th day after childbirth. This was ascribed to the violent coming of the milk and the real cause, an infection, was overlooked. In the 18thC. many upper class women did not feed their own children at all causing stasis of the milk, which was produced naturally after childbirth.

milk sickness endemic disease called 'trembles' affecting cattle which have eaten poisonous vegetation and which is communicated to humans by drinking milk or eating butter or flesh of an infected animal.

The patient is apathetic, weak, has a loathing of food and nausea. The tongue is moist and flabby and covered with a heavy white coating. Thirst is great, the patient is constipated, the breath has an offensive smell and vomiting is a frequent symptom. The patient throughout appears drowsy and a comatose condition results in a fatal end, although some cases are not so extreme and recovery takes place.

millstone grinder's asthma (see pneumoconiosis).

miner's elbow bursa of the elbow (see housemaid's knee).

When hewing at the coal face, the miner leans on his elbow causing constant pressure on the joint.

miner's nystagmus problem with eyesight caused or aggravated by mental stress.

The movement of the eyeball is very jerky when attempts are made to look sideways (nystagmus). The disease progresses through dimness of vision to total blindness along with giddiness, sensitiveness to light, depression, night blindness, sleeplessness, spasms of the eyelids, pain in the head and a tremor.

First reported in Derbyshire by coal miners in the 1890's this new disease was said by a local doctor to be caused by the poor quality of safety lamps. The mine owners refused to replace the lamps after a Sheffield eye surgeon concluded that this was not the cause and a furious row errupted between the unions and the mine owners. This was reported in national newspapers and the 'disease' spread beyond Derbyshire. The arguments continued until 1907 when the disease was recognised as one for which compensation was available but by 1913 the diagnosis was being made on any one of the above symptoms even in the absence of true nystagmus. From then on the compensation claims steadily increased, in 1908 there were 460 new cases diagnised, by 1919

there were 6,449 new cases and by 1938 there were 10,638 cases and 1.4% of all underground miners in the UK were affected including the founder of the National Health Service Aneurin Bevan. Throughout this time the disputes about the condition continued and it was gradually accepted that it was a stress related condition and disappeared as a disease during the 1940's and 1950's.

miscarriage spontaneous delivery of a foetus or the products of conception before the 24th week of pregnancy. (see abortion).

mitral disease disease of the mitral valve of the heart between the left auricle (upper chamber) and left ventricle (lower chamber) often caused by rheumatic fever.

mitral incompetence failure of the mitral valve to close properly due to disease.

mitral regurgitation failure of the mitral valve to close properly allowing blood to flow back from the ventricle to the auricle.

mitral stenosis narrowing of the opening of the mitral valve thus obstructing the flow of blood between the left chambers of the heart.

modified smallpox smallpox as altered by vaccination to be a less virulent disease.

The symptoms are similar to smallpox but are much milder and only flourish for a few days after which the patient begins to recover.

mongol Down's syndrome is a genetic abnormality causing mental retardation

The cause was not discovered until the 1960's and a test is now offered to pregnant women to assess their risk of having a Down's Syndrome baby.

morbilli measles.

morbus Brightii (see Bright's disease).

morbus Latin name for disease.

morbus cordis Latin name for heart disease.

morbus Gallicus French disease (see syphilis).

morbus Neapolitonus Italian disease (see syphilis).

mortification (see gangrene).

motions (see faeces).

mower's mite (see harvest mite).

mucous membrane the lining of the mouth, nose, throat, air passages, urinary and genital organs.

The membranes secrete a thick sticky fluid to keep the surfaces moist.

multiple sclerosis (see disseminated sclerosis).

mumps an infectious disease seen in epidemics usually in childhood but also seen in young adults.

The first signs are headache, high temperature and sore throat followed by swelling of the parotid glands on either side of the neck. Complications include deafness, inflammation of the testes in boys which can cause sterility, inflammation of the breast, ovaries or pancreas or inflammation of the brain which was usually fatal. A vaccine to prevent the disease was introduced in 1967.

mundify cleanse.

mushroom worker's lung hypersensitivity to the spores of mushrooms. (see extrisnic allergic alveolitis).

myasthenia gravis slow progressive disease causing facial paralysis affecting the eye, facial and shoulder muscles and occasionally the legs.

Paralysis of the eye muscles leads to squints, double vision, drooping eyelids and weakness of facial muscles causing a peculiar lack of expression and typical 'snarling' smile. Death occurs after many years due to inolvement of the respiratory muscles.

myelo-meningecele (see spina bifida).

myocardial degeneration (see heart failure).

myocardial fibrosis conversion of the heart muscle into fibrous tissue.

Fibrous tissue is not as elastic as muscle, therefore the heart cannot pump efficiently.

myocardial infarction heart attack.

myocarditis inflammation of the heart muscle - the myocardium.

nauill navel.

nausea a feeling that vomiting is about to take place.

neapolitan fever (see brucellosis).

nease sneeze.

necrosis (see gangrene).

necrosis of the tibia (see periostitis).

neonatal tetanus (see tetanus neonatorum).

nephralgia pain in one or both kidneys.

nephritis inflammation of a kidney.

This can follow any infection caused by a bacteria known as streptococcus.

nervous cholick frequently termed the 'dry belly-ache'. It often continues several days with little urine passed and obstinate constipation.

nervous fever or slow fever - a form of depression.

It was said to be common among persons of a weak relaxed habit who neglect exercise, live on a poor watery diet such as unripe fruits, cucumbers, melons, mushrooms etc., study hard or indulge in spirituous liquors. It was a very common disease in the rainy seasons and proved fatal to those who lived in dirty houses, crowded streets, hospitals and jails. It was also induced by keeping on wet clothes or lying on damp ground. Symptoms included low spirits, poor appetite, weakness and weariness, watchfulness, deep sighing, a quick weak pulse, dry tongue, alternating chilliness and flushing. Patients then complained of giddiness, pain in the head, nausea and vomiting, they passed pale urine and had difficulty breathing and a slight delirium. Towards the 9th-12th day, if large pustules broke out on the lips and nose or the ears began to discharge, there was a favourable outcome to the disease, but if there was excessive diarrhoea, fainting fits, trembling of the tongue, loss of sight and hearing and involuntary discharging of urine and faeces then the outcome was fatal.

nettle rash (see urticaria).

neuralgia nerve pain.

The actual cause of this is not clearly traceable. It occurs in persons suffering from gout or rheumatism, malnutrition, anaemia, syphilis or malaria. The pain is generally localised to one area but may spread. It can vary in intensity and often occurs at certain times of the day or night. There may be over sensitiveness of the skin, loss of feeling, paralysis, wasting of muscles or whitening of the hair. Attacks occur when general health is poor.

neuritis inflammation of a nerve.

noma (see cancrum oris).

Norwegian scabies Scottish name given to a severe form of scabies in which the skin becomes very thickened and deep crevices develope.

nutmeg liver chronic congestion of the liver due to heart failure or chronic lung disease often called fatty infiltration. The liver is enlarged due to an increased venous blood supply which compresses the cells and causes atrophy. A brown pigment is sometimes deposited on the surface which shows a network of dilated and distended blood vessels with pale areas in between giving the liver a mottled appearance like that of a nutmeg. The circulation becomes sluggish and fibrous tissue forms. The abdomen will feel full and tender and diarrhoea, hematemasis, jaundice, ascites and general dropsy may occur. The faeces become clay coloured and the urine is dark.

obstetrics a branch of medicine caring for women during pregnancy, labour and childbirth and into the first month after delivery.

obstetrician doctor specializing in obstetrics.

obstruction in the bowel means a stoppage to the passage of partially digested food down the intestine caused by a hernia, the pressure of tumours in neighbouring organs, intussusception or the stone of a large fruit or a mass of hardened faeces.
It is severe abdominal pain which comes and goes and is accompanied by vomiting, constipation and swelling and tenderness of the abdomen. The initial vomiting is of the contents of the stomach which is followed by yellow or green bitter bile. After several hours it becomes brown and foul smelling as the contents of the bowels are vomited. In the later stages of the disease the patient will collapse although consciousness is usually retained until death which occurs in 3-6 days.

oedema (see dropsy) accumulation of fluid beneath the skin.

omentum a fold in the peritoneum which is the membrane covering the abdominal cavity which contains fat and keeps the intestines warm and reduces friction.

omphalitis inflammation of the umbilicus and cellulitis of the abdominal wall surrounding it arising 2-3 weeks after birth.
There is redness and swelling of the area and the infection may spread to the peritoneum. The condition may resolve without problems or an abscess may form leading to gangrene.

ophthalmia infectious inflammation of the eyes.
It is a very painful condition in which the eyes become red and swollen. The patient is not able to bear light and there is usually a prickling sensation as if the eyes are filled with grit resulting in hot tears or rheum running down the cheeks. In the $18^{th}C$. it was said to be caused by long exposure to the night air, viewing snow or other bright objects, reading or writing long into the night by candle light, drinking spiritous liquors or an excess of venery (sex!). Suggested initial treatment was bleeding ten or twelve ounces of blood from the jugular vein.

ophthalmia neonatorum appears a few days after birth to a child whose mother is suffering from gonorrhoea.
The infected vaginal discharges of the mother infect the child's eyes as it is being born and was once responsible for 50% of blindness in children.

osteoarthritis chronic rheumatic arthritis the most common disorder of the joints said to affect 80%-90% of people over the age of 60 years.

It is characterised by pain and stiffness of one or more joints accompanied by deformity of the bone as new bone grows around the diseased one. A summary of the treatment in the 1970's states 'The obvious thing to do is to 'spare' the joints, just as one spares a horse that is 'a bit gone in the forelegs' or a car with a worn transmission'.

osteomyelitis inflammation of the centre of a bone, the marrow, caused by bacteria.

It is usually caused by injury or deep ulcers and was untreatable until the discovery of antibiotics.

otitis media (see middle ear disease).

ovarian tumour cancer in the female ovary.

It is a condition which is difficult to diagnose until at an advanced stage and untreatable until the discovery of anaesthetics for surgery.

overflowing of the gall bladder diarrhoea from an excess of bile in the bowel usually caused by disease such as cancer in the lower end of the small intestine.

overlaid child who has been suffocated when laid upon by a sleeping adult.

It was a common cause of death of babies and young children in overcrowded housing conditions. In 1906 the British Medical Journal stated that 1,000 infants die every year in London alone, a frequent cause being the intoxication of the mother.

painter's colic lead poisoning.

The extensive use of lead in the preparation of coloured paint creates a special liability in painters to suffer from lead poisoning and painters colic is a common manifestation. Symptoms begin with a disturbance in digestion, anaemia, loss of flesh, constipation and colic. A blue line appears at the roots of the teeth which is interrupted if a tooth is missing. Cramps occur in the muscles and paralysis and dropped wrists

occur. Pains in joints and a gouty condition may arise. The arteries are hardened and nephritis is common. Loss of consciousness and fits may usher in a fatal end.

palpitations a condition in which the heart beats forcibly or irregularly and the person becomes conscious of its action.

It can occur at puberty at the menopause or if the body is already weakened by anaemia, fever or nervous exhaustion. Sudden emotions such as fright or indigestion may bring on an attack as well as overuse of tea, coffee or alcohol.

palsy weakness or paralysis of a limb or part of the body such as the face.

paludism (see ague).

pancreatitis inflammation of the pancreas.

This is a long flat gland lying behind the stomach supplying juices to the small intestine which aid digestion. It is also responsible for the secretion of insulin.

papilloma a benign tumour growing from skin or mucous membrane

When growing from the skin it is a hard tumour called a wart; When growing from mucous membrane it is a delicate mass of branching filaments. These tumours may become malignant.

papule (see pimple).

paralytic ileus paralysis of part of the small intestine due to inadequate muscular activity which results in obstruction of the bowels.

It usually occurs after abdominal surgery when the intestines have been subjected to much handling.

paralysis loss of function of a muscle.

It usually follows a stroke, an injury or a disease such as poliomyelitis and can affect one or more limbs, the face or the whole body.

paralysis agitans (see Parkinsons disease).

parametritis also called pelvic cellulitis.

It is an inflammation of the parametrium, the connective tissue around the womb and pelvic organs.

paraphrenitis inflammation of the diaphragm.

Symptoms include a high fever and extreme pain in the upper abdomen whenever the patient coughs, sneezes takes a breath, takes food, goes to stool or passes urine. The patient is restless, anxious and has a dry cough, hiccup and is often delirious. If suppuration occurs the outcome is fatal.

paraplegia paralysis of the legs which sometimes includes the bladder and rectum.

paratyphoid infectious disease resembling typhoid but caused by a slightly different bacteria.

Parkinson's disease caused by a degenerative disease of the brain.

It is characterised by an expressionless face, slow movements, unblinking eyes, rigidity of muscles and rythmic tremor, usually of hands. The cause is unknown.

parotitis inflammation of one of the salivary glands in the face.

It is usually the first of the glands to become enlarged in cases of mumps.

paroxysm sudden crisis, intensity of symptoms or reappearance of a disease.

The term was also used to describe a fit, spasm or convulsion.

parturition the act of giving birth to a child.

pedicullus humanus capitas head louse.

They are usually found in clean rather than dirty hair. The eggs are visible as little white specks, known as nits, which are laid in the hairs at the back of the head or behind the ears. The scratching of an infested head often leads to the hair being matted together by blood and the lymph glands at the back of the head and behind the ears are often enlarged.

pediculus humanus corporus body louse.

Lives in clothing, particularly in the seams where the eggs are laid but feeds on the blood of its host. The female lives for almost

a month laying 7-10 eggs per day during that time. The eggs hatch in 7-10 days and are fully mature in another 7 days. Without food, an adult body louse will die in around 9 days and a newly hatched louse in 2 days.

pellagra caused by a shortage of vitamin B in the diet.

This is a chronic condition causing loss of appetite, diarrhoea or constipation, headache and irritability of temper. Areas of the skin appear sunburned and as the skin peels off it leaves thick, rough, brown patches. Tremors, sleepiness and weakness of the legs occur and as the attacks become more severe the patient becomes emaciated and sometimes completely paralysed or demented. The symptoms resemble leprosy with which it was once confused.

pelosis rheumatica (see purpura rheumatica).

pemphigus severe autoimmune disease which was frequently fatal before the discovery of steroids.

It is characterised by blebs or blisters which vary in size between a millet seed and an apple and are filled with a clear yellowish or muddy fluid. The skin on which they rest is slightly inflamed and itchy. They come out in successive crops over various parts of the body except the head, palms of the hands and soles of the feet. The fluid of the blebs may be absorbed and the skin over the collapsed sac becomes dry and peels off or the bleb may burst leaving an area of raw smelly skin. The blebs increase in size and number until large areas of skin are involved and the patient becomes ill. The mouth is frequently involved with unpleasantly eroded areas making eating very painful. There are several forms of the disease and the outcome is prolonged even with today's treatments. However the side effects of the treatment can occasionally be so severe as to be fatal. The disease was once thought to be infectious and often mistaken for impetigo.

pemphigus neonatorum a term once used for bullous impetigo of a newborn infant.

The symptoms appear between 3-6 days after birth and are in proportion to the size and number of the blebs and the rapidity of their development. Where they are very large and spread rapidly death usually

follows in 2-3 days from exhaustion. A once common epidemic disease in maternity hospitals and nurseries, where the infection was spread by nurses, midwives and doctors, the mortality rate was very high. An outbreak involving 80 babies took place in Guy's Hospital in 1987. (see bullous impetigo).

penicillin common antibiotic discovered in 1929 by Sir Alexander Fleming.

percussion tapping surfaces of the body to listen for sounds or vibrations to aid diagnosis.

The practice was discovered and has been used since 1753 by a German physician. However Hippocrates was also aware of the value of the procedure.

pericardial effusion the space between the outer membrane of the heart and the heart itself becomes full of fluid caused by an infection, rheumatic fever, uraemia, tuberculosis, or injury to the chest.

The condition is characterzsed by pain over the heart, high fever, rapid, feeble pulse, restlessness, difficulty in breathing and eventually delirium and death.

pericarditis inflammation of the outer membrane of the heart, the pericardium.

The pericardium is a bag inside which the heart works. It is lubricated on the inside so that the organ can slip up and down easily with each beat. The first effect of pericarditis is failure of lubrication and friction causes the heart to rub on the side of its bag often causing intense pain. However the friction soon produces such an outflow of fluid that the bag fills up and separates the raw surfaces preventing the friction and so removing the pain for the time being. The patient is pale and often feverish and breathless but the condition is rarely fatal.

perineal carcinomatosis a spread of cancer to the perineum which is a wedge shaped muscular area between the anus and the genitals.

The main tumour would be in Corporio Uteri, the womb.

periodic fever (see ague).

periostitis inflammation of a bone.

This leads to slow absorption of healthy bone which then becomes thinner and weaker and fractures occur easily. In severe cases of inflammation as the bone tissue slowly dies it acts as an irritant and gives rise to more inflammation around it and

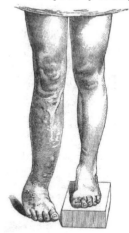

as the bone slowly disintegrates copious amounts of pus accumulates. As the inflamation increases, it cuts off the blood supply to the rest of the bone causing necrosis (gangrene). The symptoms begin with fever and general lethargy, rigors, pain in the affected limb and swelling. The skin *becomes swollen, red and shining and there is extreme tenderness until the pus erupts through the surface of the skin. This is often a relief to the patient but ususally fresh areas of pus arise elswhere in the bone and before antibiotics the condition was often fatal.*

peripneumony inflammation of the lungs.

Persons suffering from this disease usually abound with thick blood, have tense and rigid fibres and who feed upon gross aliment and drink strong viscid liquors. It is usually fatal to those who have a flat breast or narrow chest and to persons suffering from asthma. When the disease proceeds from a viscid pituitous matter obstructing the vessels of the lungs it is called spurious or bastard peripneumony but if it arises from a thin acrid defluction on the lungs, it is called catarrhal peripneumony. The symptoms are similar to those of pleurisy.

peritonitis inflammation of the membrane covering the abdominal organs. (see also rupture of bowels).

peritonsillar abscess (see quinsy).

perityphlitis (see appendicitis).

pernicious anaemia lack of vitamin B12 which is necessary for the formation of adequate numbers of red blood cells and also for the red cells to become fully mature. *Patients will be very pale and weak and often complain of a sore tongue which is inflamed and smooth. Their skin may be slightly yellow and they may have difficulty in walking and pins and needles in hands and feet.*

pertussis (see whooping cough).

peruvian bark the bark of the evergreen tree Cinchona otherwise known as quinine. *It was used for reducing fevers.*

pesill leg or haunch.

pestelence (see black death).

phagedaena a condition in which ulcers on the skin spread very rapidly and become septic.

phlebitis inflammation of a vein usually caused by infection and nearly always associated with thrombosis or blood clots in the affected vein.

phlegm sticky mucus secreted in the lungs usually during an infection. *It is one of the four humours described by Galen an excess of which made the individual sluggish and dull.*

phlegmonous tonsilitis (see quinsy).

phossy jaw destruction of the upper and lower jaw caused by long exposure to phosphorous fumes. *It was found in workers in trades which used phosphorous mainly in the early match making industry. The disease began in a hollow tooth or gum infection eventually spreading to the whole jaw leading to a discharge of pus and eventual necrosis of the bone. The amount of fumes escaping during production was regulated by the White Phosphorous Matches Prohibition Act in 1908 when white or yellow phosphorous was banned in favour of red amorphous.*

phrenitis inflammation of the brain. *It is usually found as a symptom of other fevers but often proved fatal after only a few days and if prolonged or improperly treated, it sometimes ended in madness or a kind of stupidity which continued for life. In the 18^{th}C. it was said to be caused by studying late into the night, hard drinking, anger, grief or anxiety. Also it may have been caused by stoppage of the faeces or urine, exposure to hot sun especially sleeping outside in the summer bare headed when a person may wake quite delirious. It may also be caused by external injuries to the head. The symptoms commence with pain in the head, redness of the eyes, a violent flushing of the face, disturbed sleep, great dryness of the skin, nose bleeds, singing in the ears and extreme sensitiveness of the nervous system.*

phrenzy (see frenzy).

phthirus pubis crab louse. *It attaches itself tenaciously to the hairs in the pubic area and causes intense itching. It is transmitted by sexual contact or on towels and clothing.*

phthisis means wasting and is applied to any tubercular disease causing emaciation and loss of strength.

The term is usually applied to tuberculosis of the lungs in which the disease rapidly breaks down the tissues and forms a cavity inside the lungs.

pigeon breeder's lung hypersensitivity to pigeon droppings. (see extrinsic allergic alveolitis).

pimple a solid elevation above the level of the skin between a millet seed and a lentil in size. It contains no fluid and may be of the natural colour of the skin, reddish, bluish or black. Pimples are commonly connected with the glands of the hair and their presence gives a feeling of roughness to the skin and may on occasion cause severe itching and tingling.

piss-prophet 18[th]C. quack doctor who claimed to diagnose disease by examining the urine often without ever seeing the patient.

They charged a small fee for the service but a high price for the medicines to achieve a 'cure'.

pityriasis patches of scaly, bran-like, 'dirty brown' areas occuring on the upper trunk, arms and neck, caused by a fungal infection.

placenta the organ attached to the wall of the womb and then to the foetus by the umbilical cord during pregnancy.

It performs the functions of nutrition, respiration and excretion until the child is born.

placenta praevia condition occurring in pregnancy when the placenta develops in the lower part of the womb.

If undiagnosed before labour starts and a caesarian section is not performed, heavy bleeding will occur before the birth leading to the death of the child and often the mother.

plasterer's itch similar condition to bricklayer's itch.

It also produces stiffness, swelling and pain of the affected part. The skin peels and the nails become thin, brittle and ribbed.

plethorick having excess blood circulating in the body.

pleuropneumonia combination of pleurisy and pneumonia.

pleurisy painful inflammation of the membranes covering the lungs.

It was once thought to be caused by drinking cold liquors when the body was hot, by cold northerly winds, by violent exercise such as running, wrestling, leaping, supporting a great weight, or blows on the breast. Symptoms begin with chilliness and shivering which are followed by fever, thirst and restlessness and a violent pricking pain in one side which sometimes radiates towards the spine and sometimes towards the shoulder blades and is most great when the patient breathes in.

pneumococcal meningitis usually secondary to a pneumococcal infection elsewhere in the body such as an abscess, pneumonia or otitis media.

It was usually fatal until the discovery of antibiotics.

pneumoconiosis term applied to a chronic form of inflammation of the lungs which affects workers who constantly inhale irritating particles.

It causes permanent alteration in the structure of the lungs so that they do not expand properly and there are three chief varieties: anthracosis from inhaling coal dust; siderosis from inhaling fine metalic particles in tin, copper, lead and iron mines and from grinding or turning steel; silicosis from the particles in quartz and slate quarries and in the pottery trade.

pneumonia inflammation of the lungs caused by bacteria or viruses causing fluid to collect in the air sacs of the lungs or by the inhalation of fluid into the lungs during vomiting.

The lungs then become hard and solid making breathing very painful. The symptoms include sore throat, wheezing, and in a young child a high fever. Elderly patients may become seriously ill very quickly with no fever but confusion is commonly seen. It is still a fatal disease in the very young or elderly.

pneumonic plague highly infectious variant of bubonic plague which was spread from person to person by droplet infection and attacked the lungs. *Sufferers were usually dead within 3 days of catching the infection.*

podagra (see gout).

polio poliomyelitis a viral infection of the central nervous system causing permanent paralysis.

The disease is caught by swallowing infected food or water or by eating with unwashed contaminated hands. The onset is sudden about 4 days after contracting the disease. The first symptom is a convulsion followed by fever, headache, vomiting and pain in one or more limbs. After 1-3 days it is noticed that the child does not move one or more of its limbs and the paralysis may spread rapidly to the muscles of the trunk. If the paralysis spreads to the nerves of the muscles of the chest, death occurs from failure of the respiratory system. If the child survives it may have permanently paralysed limbs. As the child grows the parylised muscles remain weak and withered and the limb is shrunken as the bones fail to grow. If the largest part of the infection has occurred in the brain the child suffers from violent and frequently recurring convulsions which may last 12 hours or more. These are succeeded by a drowsy stage often lasting several days during which widespread paralysis affecting one or both sides of the body may have occurred. Once a worldwide disease, it is now confined to third world countries due to vaccination which was introduced in 1953.

pooss a cough.

portal vein carries blood from the stomach, intestines and spleen to the liver.

posette a drink made from milk curdled with ale or wine and given to invalids.

post-partum haemorrhage excessive bleeding after the birth of a child, during the expulsion of the afterbirth or within 24 hours.

It is due to prolonged labour, numerous previous pregnancies, anaemia, too rapid a delivery of the infant, fibroids or mismanagement of the delivery.

potter's asthma (see chalicosis).

potter's rot (see chalicosis).

pox (see syphilis).

premature birth baby born alive before 37 completed weeks of pregnancy (usual length of pregnancy 40 weeks).

The previous definition of prematurity was an infant weighing less than 2,640 gramms (5lb 8oz). Such infants are now classed as low birth weight infants as they can be born at full term and still be below 2,640 gramms.

prolapsus uteri descent of the uterus (womb). In the early stages part of the bladder or bowel may protrude through the vagina and in the later stages the womb itself is visible.

It is caused usually by lax muscles in the pelvic area due to frequent or difficult childbearing.

prostatectomy surgical operation to remove the male prostate gland.

It is usually performed in cases of cancer.

prostatic obstruction enlargement of the male prostate gland, which is situated at the base of the bladder, causing an obstruction to the passage of urine.

This condition would be caused by either a benign or malignant tumour.

prostatitis inflammation of the male prostate gland.

psoas abscess tuberculosis of the spine where the infection spreads down the psoas muscle from the middle of the spine to the thigh bone (femur) causing an abscess in the groin.

The leg would be oedematous, permanently bent and covered with erysipelas.

psoriasis chronic non-infectious inflammatory skin disease characterized by scaly red patches mainly on knees, elbows and scalp.

puerperal fever (see childbed fever).

puerperal peritonitis childbed fever which spreads to the surrounding lymphatic vessels and veins in the pelvic cavity causing peritonitis.

pulmonaris lung disease.

pulmonary anthrax (see anthrax).

The lungs may be infected by the inhalation of infected dust. The symptoms are like those of pneumonia with grave constitutional disturbance. The disease is difficult to diagnose which gives little hope of recovery.

pulmonary apoplexy haemorrhage into the lungs from either heart or lung disease.

pulmonary congestion abnormal collection of fluid in the lungs.

It could be caused by pneumonia, pleurisy or heart failure.

pulmonary embolism blood clot in the lungs.

pulmonary hypertension high blood pressure in the pulmonary artery, the main artery supplying oxygen to the lungs.

The cause of this relatively rare disease is not known but it is often found in lung diseases such as emphysema. The high blood pressure causes damage to the right ventricle of the heart preventing it from pumping blood efficiently to the lungs. The symptoms are similar to heart failure and include shortness of breath, swollen ankles, pulse, chest pain or discomfort, dizziness and general fatigue.

pulmonary phthisis tuberculosis of the lungs.

pulmonary thrombosis blood clot in the lungs.

purging emptying of the stomach or bowel by giving a vomit provoking agent or an enema.

This was usually the first line treatment for any disease or illness, along with bleeding.

purpura small red patches of bleeding into the skin and the tissues just under the skin without external injury.

It is sometimes a symptom of scurvy or haemophilia. It is also commonly found in the elderly.

purpura haemorrhagica usually occurs in young fragile girls.

It begins suddenly with fever, headache, generalised pains and weakness. The macules are larger than in other forms of purpura and tend to merge together. The mucous membranes are always involved and there may be bleeding from the nose, mouth, throat, stomach, lungs, bowels and kidneys. Internal bleeding may also occur as well as bleeding in the membranes of the brain or into the brain itself with fatal consequences. The disease usually takes 6-8 weeks to subside but can last for many months with repeated haemorrhages making the patient dangerously anaemic.

purpura neonatorum occurs in cases of congenital syphilis and is usually fatal.

purpura rheumatica a more serious form of the disease.

It begins with a short period of intermittent fever accompanied by pains in the bones, joints and muscles and by headache and weariness. Soon after this a crop of macules appear on the legs varying in size from 1cm to 5cm. The macules are a dusky red colour and soon spread to the chest, back, arms and occasionally the face. The mucous membranes are sometimes affected and occasionally complications in the form of haemorrhages from the bowels and kidneys along with a return of the fever and vomiting.

purpura simplex common in children and usually associated with any type of feverish illness.

Numerous tiny haemorrhages occur chiefly on the legs, sometimes accompanied by stiffness of the joints. The spots disappear after a few weeks leaving no trace.

purulent mucus or liquid containing pus.

pus thick fluid formed by the action of pyogenic or pus forming organisms on the tissues of the body.

When harmful bacteria invade any part of the body there is an immediate reaction resulting in an increased blood supply to the area. Certain cells (leucocytes), normally contained in the blood, leave the blood vessels and are attracted to the damaged area. These cells have the power to engulf and destroy the harmful bacteria but if the bacteria are too numerous or too virulent the leucocytes themselves are killed and the surrounding tissues, now unprotected, are destroyed. The pus formed by this process therefore consists of large numbers of dead and dying leucocytes.

pushes old term for pimples.

pustular tetter (see impetigo).

pustule is the same as a vesicle but instead of clear fluid it contains yellow matter - pus. *A vesicle becomes a pustule if the clear contents become infected and turn into pus.*

putrefication change which takes place in the bodies of animals after death. *It is decomposition.*

putrid or spotted fever term which was used for both typhoid fever and meningococcal meningitis.

putrid or ulcerous sore throat (see malignant quinsy).

pyaemia a disease whereby pus-secreting micro-organisms, usually from an abscess, get into the blood supply and lodge in any area causing the formation of another abscess.

pyogenic meningitis occurs secondary to other infections such as influenza, gonorrhoea or anthrax.

pyelitis inflammation of the basin shaped part or pelvis of the kidney.

pyelonephritis inflammation of the whole of the kidney.

pyloric stenosis narrowing of the entrance to the stomach, the pylorus, which becomes thickened and enlarged through muscle spasms. *This congenital condition is usually found in male babies around the age of 10 days. They begin to vomit after every feed and the* *vomitus is forcibly expelled for some distance. The baby is hungry and greedy for his feeds but as he is getting no nourishment soon becomes malnourished. There is progressive loss of weight and strength and death is a state of extreme marasmus, the vomiting continuing to the end. The condition today can be treated surgically. If the patient is an adult the cause may be due to a stomach ulcer or tumour.*

pylorus the opening of the stomach into the duodenum.

pyonephrosis pus in the kidney.

pyosalpinx peritonitis abscess in the fallopian tube which bursts and causes general peritonitis. *This could be caused by an ectopic pregnancy.*

quack doctor (see empiric).

quartan ague an ague which misses two days before recurring.

quickening the first feeling of foetal movements by a pregnant woman. *With a first pregnancy this is felt at 14 weeks duration but with subsequent pregnancies can be as early as 12 weeks. The quickening was believed to be the time when the soul entered the body of the infant and was once used as a prediction of the time the baby was due to be born.*

quinsy abscess on the tonsils which spreads to the adjacent tissues. *The consequent swelling and oedema cause severe pain and inability to swallow saliva and the patient spits out a sticky phlegm. . As the swelling and inflammation increase, breathing becomes difficult, there is pain in the ears, the eyes become red and the face swells. The patient is often obliged to keep upright to prevent suffocation. There is constant nausea and vomiting and fluid cannot be swallowed and returns down the nose. The patient is frequently starved to death merely from an inability to swallow food and drink. However if the quinsy is present alongside another disease, the patient will already be weak and frothing at* *the mouth, as well as having swollen tongue, pale, ghastly countenance and coldness of extremities. These are all fatal signs.*

rabies viral infection of the nervous system caught by a bite from an infected animal.

The virus immediately attacks the nerve endings and entering the nervous system progresses towards the brain. The nearer the wound is to the brain i.e. the face, the shorter the incubation period. There is pain and irritation at the site of the wound and the patient is haunted by fear of water. The pain spreads throughout the body and the patient is tormented by thirst but on attempting to swallow a suffocating spasm of the larynx occurs which contorts the face. Spasms are also brought on by sounds or by a breath of air on the skin. At first they last a few mnutes but later extend to 15-20 minutes. The patient has frenzies of screaming, throws himself about, beats his hands upon his chest and attacks bystanders. The eyes roll and the mouth remains open and saliva pours out as they remain unable to swallow. A fever develops along with a hoarse voice and a fast erratic pulse. Sometimes there is acute mania but generally recovery takes place between attacks. However this stage lasts only 2 days and the patient then falls into unconsciousness and dies. The disease is still fatal unless patients are fully vaccinated or a vaccine is administered within 24 hours of being bitten. A vaccine was first discovered used successfully on a 9 year old boy in 1885 by Louis Pasteur.

rachitis (see rickets).

rag sorter's disease (see pulmonary anthrax).

railway spine an old term referring to a special morbid nervous condition arising after an accident.

In some cases, especially after railway accidents, symptoms ensue somewhat similar to those of concussion of the spine but arising from a different cause. The condition usually occurs at an interval after the accident and is in reality a neurotic manifestation which as a rule recovers completely after the worries of legal compensation have been settled.

reines or raynes old name for the kidneys.

relapsing fever (see remitting fever).

relaxed bowels diarrhoea.

In 1721 William Buchan describes this in children and attributes it to many diseases such as rickets and scrophula. He says it is caused by poor diet where children are fed entirely on slops i.e. soft food instead of solids.

relaxed throat (see clergyman's throat).

remitting fever a malarious fever.

It is characterised by irregular repeated exacerbations and remission of symptoms which occur around the 8th day. The patient feels much improved but within a few hours the fever returns. Symptoms begin with yawning, stretching, pain and giddiness in the head, alternate fits of heat and cold and delirium. There is pain and swelling of the abdomen, the tongue is white and the skin and eyes are yellow, the patient is also afflicted with bilious vomiting.

renal calculi kidney stones.

They may not cause any symptoms but if they move they can prevent the proper functioning of the kidney and surgical removal is required.

renal colic acute abdominal pain occurring in spasms due to kidney stones passing through the ureters which are the tubes linking the kidneys to the bladder.

retroperitoneal sarcoma cancer of the tissues behind the peritoneum which is the membrane lining the inside of the abdomen .

rheum discharge from the eyes due to infection (see opthalmia).

rheumatic fever infection causing a fever that results in lesions in the heart, blood vessels or joints.

The fibrous tissue around the joints is very painful and many of the joints are affected either at the same time or in succession.

This can follow any infection by a bacteria known as streptococcus.

rheumatic gout rheumatoid arthritis.

Rheumatism, rheumatoid arthritis and gout were once thought to be the same disease. It was not until 1803 that rheumatoid arthritis was recognised as a distinct disease. Throughout the 19thC. medical opinion was divided as to whether there was a relationship between the three diseases and the term rheumatic gout was therefore applied to rheumatoid arthritis.

rheumatism chronic inflammatory disease causing pain and deformity in joints, and lack of mobility.

rheumatoid arthritis one of the most crippling of all rheumatic diseases.

Beginning very gradually with pain, redness and swelling of the affected joints, it tends to begin in small joints such as the fingers and attacks are accompanied by a high temperature, rapid pulse, loss of appetite, sweating and general prostration. With recurrent attacks the affected joints become chronically swollen and fixed causing characteristic deformity.

rheumatoid endocarditis endocarditis caused by rheumatic fever.

rickets childhood disease caused by lack of vitamin D, fresh air and sunlight which in turn causes abnormal bone development.

The disease is characterised by a large head, narrow chest, prominent abdomen, swellings of the wrists and ankles and curvature of the long bones of the arms and legs. Early symptoms include severe sweating of the head during sleep, extreme restlessness at night and constipation. Nodules appear on all the ribs (rachitic rosary) sometimes visible and as large as marbles. The deformities are usually numerous and in extreme cases affect every bone in the body. The muscles and ligaments are poorly developed and flabby and the child is unable to sit erect, stand or walk at the appropriate age. The muscles of the abdomen are also very lax giving rise to a typical 'pot belly'. Anaemia is present and

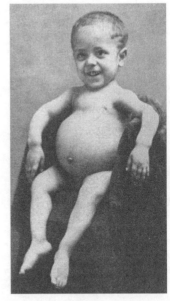

although rickets itself is rarely fatal the cachexia it produces predisposes the infant to catching all childhood diseases.

rigor attack of shivering although the patient has a high temperature.

Often seen at the height of a disease or fever.

ringworm (see tinea capitas and barbers rash).

rock fever (see brucellosis).

rose rash false measles.

An eruption of red patches on the chest and neck and sometimes on the face and arms. They fade on pressure but reappear on removing the pressure. Lasting only a few days, they soon fade and often slight shedding of the skin occurs. Before and during the eruption feverishness, headache and disturbances of digestion occur and the disease is apt to be mistaken for measles or scarlet fever but it is not contagious and lasts only a day or two.

roseola term used in the 19thC. and early 20thC. for any rose coloured rash.

Epidemic roseola was used to describe German measles. Roseola infantilis (see gum rash). Roseola vaccinia a rash which sometimes occurs after vaccination.

roundworms resemble small earthworms and live in the small intestines of infected persons.

There are usually only two or three and may be ten to twelve inches long. They cause no

problems unless there are large numbers when they give rise to abdominal pain, diarrhoea and vomiting.

rubella an infectious disease prevelant in spring and early summer.

It is a much milder disease than measles commencing with lethargy, headache, nasal catarrh and a slight temperature. A dusky pink rash appears on the 2nd day of the illness and is first seen on the forehead and behind the ears before spreading to the trunk and limbs. It lasts only 2 days and complications are rare unless the disease is caught during the first 3 months of pregnancy when the foetus may develop congenital heart disease or be born blind, deaf and dumb. A vaccine was introduced in 1970.

rubeola a term used in the 19^{th}C. and early 20^{th}C. for measles, german measles and scarlet fever.

rupture see hernia.

rupture of bowels or perforation may take place as a result of injury or disease.

Ulceration such as that found in typhoid fever or appendicitis or occasionally in tuberculosis may cause an opening in the bowel walls. The contents of the bowel pass out into the abdominal cavity causing peritonitis which causes severe pain. After a few hours the abdomen swells and becomes very tender to touch. The patient begins vomiting and passes into a state of collapse and death occurs within 2-3 days.

salpingitis inflammation of the Fallopian tubes.

sanatorium an institution for convalescent patients.

Term usually applied to hospitals for the open-air treatment of tuberculosis.

sangina (see angina).

sarcoma cancer of the connective or supportive tissue such as bone, muscle, cartilage, fibrous tissues or blood vessels.

A rare form of cancer which can be found in children as well as adults, usually in the jaws (see picture), the skull and long bones. Most grow rapidly and fatally.

scabies parasitic mite caught by close contact with an infected person.

The male mite dies after mating and the female mite burrows into the skin laying 25-30 eggs on the way. The eggs hatch into larvae in 4-5 days

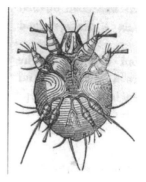

and their movement under the skin causes intense itching. The larvae then leave the burrows and develop in the skin where a female will become mature in 2-3 weeks and begin burrowing to lay her own eggs.

scald head (see tinea capitas).
The term comes from an Icelandic word meaning bald.

scalded skin syndrome (see toxic epidermal necrolysis, bullous impetigo and pemphagus neonatorum).

scarlet fever once common highly infectious childhood disease first described and given its name in 1675.
It is characterised by a sore throat, fever, vomiting and headache. A bright red rash appears around the neck and chest then spreads all over the body except the face. The rash blanches with pressure and fades after a week when the skin peels off in large shreads. Serious complications in the later stages of the disease are dropsy and a reduction in the quantity of urine secreted by the kidneys, permanent deafness, diseases of the joints and enlarged glands. In the 19ᵗʰC. it was called 'the English plague' and was caught from infected milk. Malignant scarlet fever is a much more severe form of the disease when blood poisoning is also present and was usually fatal.

scarlatina (see scarlet fever).

scarify make a series of small incisions in the skin.
The treatment used for blood-letting instead of opening a vein or cupping. A special tool called a scarificator was used consisting of a small box fitted with numerous tiny blades which was scratched across the surface of the skin.

sciatica severe pain down one or both legs along the sciatic nerve caused by injury or inflammation to the nerve or its roots in the spinal column.
The course of the sciatic nerve in the back and outer part of the thigh and various parts of the leg and foot is frequently the seat of a violent pain accompanied by tingling and numbness. It is usually increased by any sudden movement or pressure or even coughing but occasionally spasms of pain occur without any evident cause.

scirrhous a hard cancer.
Characterised by the hardness of the primary tumour and by a tendency to draw into itself neighbouring soft tissues. When ulcerated the sore is usually deep, uneven and bounded by an outward turning thick edge.

sclerosis hardening.

scorbutus (see scurvy).

scrofula (see evill).

scrum-pox (see impetigo).

scurvy a chronic disease due to deficiency of Vitamin C in the diet.

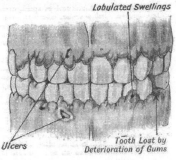

This disease was once a common cause of death among sailors and was found in prisons and workhouses due to the lack of fresh fruit and vegabales. It is characterised by sponginess and bleeding under the skin and soft tissues of the mouth and swelling of the gums. Often there is ulceration and in consequence of these changes the teeth may drop out. Swelling of the joints occurs especially the knees and ankles and there is often slight paralysis of the legs and general cachexia and anaemia.

seat-worm (see threadworm).

secundine (see placenta).

seizure sudden onset or recurrence of a disease or an attack of a pre-existing condition
The term is usually applied to an epileptic attack or a convulsion.

self abortion removal of a foetus from a pregnant womb by illegal methods.

Knitting needles or other sharp objects were frequently used resulting in a perforated womb, haemorrhage and blood poisoning. Slippery elm bark was used to open up the entrance to the womb to encourage an abortion. Women would either seek an abortionist, a woman from the village or attempt a procedure themselves. (see abortion).

senectus old age.

senile atheroma advanced arteriosclerosis of old age where complete blockage of a blood vessel results in gangrene of the area.

senile debility (see senile decay).

senile decay degenerative changes in the brain due to advancing age.
It causes severe memory loss.

senile gangrene advanced case of arteriosclerosis where there is complete obstruction of an already partially blocked vessel, usually occurs in elderly people hence the name.

sepsis/septic severe toxic state with high temperature resulting from infection with pus forming micro-organisms.

septic arthritis an infection in a joint either from direct invasion or via a blood stream infection.
This results in acute inflammation, swelling, tenderness and pain. The patient is severely ill with a high fever and without antibiotics the condition is usually fatal.

septic tonsillitis see catarrhal tonsilitis.

septicaemia severe bacterial infection of the blood stream
It was fatal until the discovery of antibiotics.

septicaemic plague was much rarer than bubonic or pneumonic plague but because of generalised blood poisoning death occurred within 24 hours before there was any time for any other symptoms of the disease to appear.

septic poisoning (see septicemia).

serous apoplexy stroke caused by oedema of the brain.

serous cholera (see Asiatic cholera).

serous effusion of the brain oedema of the brain.

seven day fever (see remitting fever).

shingles viral infection almost indistinguishable from chickenpox which attacks adults.
The symptoms begin with fever and the patient feels unwell for several days. Tiny blebs then begin to appear and as the virus invades the root of a nerve the blebs follow thetrack of the nerve on the surface of the skin. The spinal nerves are especially infected causing the blebs to appear half way round the chest and from where the disease gets it's name, shingles is Greek for girdle. The face is also very often infected from the 5th cranial nerve. The blebs increase in number for several days and the area is intensely painful. The blebs dry up and fall off after 1-2 weeks leaving tiny scars however the underlying pain may continue for anything up to one year especially in the elderly. An infected adult may pass on the disease to a child who will subsequently develop chickenpox.

shock deficiency in the volume of blood reaching the heart due to severe bleeding, injuries, infection or pain.

sibbens an old term for a disease occuring in Scotland many years ago which was possibly syphilis.

silicosis (see grinder's asthma).

sleeping sickness disease prevalent in West and Central Africa and the upper Nile basin.
A microscopic parasite is conveyed to humans by the bite of the tsetse fly. The parasite then grows in the blood and lymphatic systems causing inflammation of the small vessels in the brain. It is characterised by weakness, lethargy and an increasing tendency to sleep with gradual wasting of the body and eventually death.

sleepy sickness (see encephalitis lethargica).

small-pox highly infectious disease.

It was marked by a fever beginning 12-14 days after catching the disease and the eruption of red spots on the third day. These enlarged and became filled with clear fluid which gradually changed to a thick yellow matter on the 8th or 9th day. At this point there was much swelling, an inflammation of the surrounding skin with a very offensive odour if the pustules ruptured. The pustules covered all parts of the skin as well as the mucous membranes of the mouth, throat, nose and eyes leading to painful swallowing, difficulty breathing and sometimes blindness. The fever abated around the third day but returned as the pustules formed on the 8th or 9th day and was accompanied by restlessness, delirium or coma. The drying process then began accompanied by a great itching and the scabs dropped off between the 15th-20th day leaving pock marks according to the severity of the disease. It was regarded with horror throughout history because of its severely disfiguring effects and as a cause of death. Smallpox was described by Rhazes a $10^{th}C$. Arabic doctor and has been known in England since at least the $13^{th}C$. It was considered the scourge of Europe in the $18^{th}C$. and one in every twelve deaths in London were said to be caused by smallpox. The most likely persons to be seized with the disease were thought to be children who had over- heated themselves by running, wrestling etc., or adults after a debauch. The spots or pustules could be cut short in their development by vaccination or a previous attack of small pox from which the patient had recovered A vaccine was discovered in 1798 and smallpox was eradicated from most of the planet by 1977.

softening of the brain softening due to the blood supply to the brain being cut off or diminished.
If the blood supply is cut off by a blood clot the symptoms occur suddenly and paralysis may occur down part or one side of the body. Complete recovery may take place but if only partial recovery the intellect is impaired and the patient becomes childish and feeble surviving for some time before becoming unconscious prior to death. The softening of the brain may occur more slowly and be accompanied by weakening intellectual powers and loss of faculties, depression of spirits and a tendency to weep at any small excitement. There is pain in the head and giddiness and pain, pricking or twitching of the limbs i.e. the general decline of old age. In 1869 the disease in children was said to be due to imperfect nutrition.

Soldier's heart name given to a group of symptoms occurring during the American Civil War and again in the Great War.
There are symptoms of breathlessness on exertion or emotion, pain over the area of the heart, palpitations and exhaustion. The condition was also known as 'disordered action of the heart'.

soot cancer affected the scrotum of small boys sent up chimneys to sweep.
It appears like an irregular fungating and warty mass which is very slow growing. Surgery is the only treatment.

sore throat usually caused by a viral infection causing malaise and fever. (see quinsy, diphtheria, tonsillitis).

Spanish flu epidemic of influenza which swept the UK in 1918/9 killing more people than had been lost in WWI.

spasm involuntary painful contraction of a muscle or a hollow organ with a muscular wall.

spasm of the glottis (see laryngismus stridulus).

spasmodic cholera (see Asiatic cholera).

spasmodic croup (see laryngismus stridulus).

sphygmomanometer human blood pressure was first recorded in 1847 by a Kymograph (Greek for wave writer) invented by Carl Ludwig. After several variations a mercury sphygmomanom- eter, the prototype of today's machines, was developed in 1896 by an Italian, Scipione Riva-Rocci, and modified by an American Harvey Cushing in 1901 after which it became a commonly used instrument in medicine.

spina bifida incomplete closure of the spinal cord canal during pregnancy and at birth a hernia containing spinal fluid and sometimes nervous tissue protrudes, usually at the lower part of the spine.

It was not until the 1970's that surgery to

correct this defect was perfected and in 1980 there were still 2,500 babies born alive in England and Wales with this condition. It is now known that taking a folic acid suppliment prior to and during the first three months of pregnancy greatly reduces the chances of this defect occurring. It is also detectable in the early stages of pregnancy but babies with this condition usually died well into the 1960's.

spina bifida oculta as above but without the protruding hernia.

This condition is usually only diagnosed by x-ray although sometimes a small hairy patch or dimple is visible on the lower part of the infant's back.

spinal caries slow compression of the spinal cord due to tubercular disease. *Patients were treated by immobilising the spine in a plaster cast for many months and good nursing care was needed to prevent pressure*

sores and urinary infections from developing. Occasionally patients were operated on and a bone graft performed.

spinal concussion a severe blow upon the vertibral column causing concussion may produce serious symptoms even when there is no demonstrable fracture or dislocation. *These symptoms take the form of paralytic phenomena and general indications of shock. The patient will show either paralysis or weakness of the muscles of the body and limbs which derive their nerve supply from below the site of the injury.*

spinal meningitis inflammation of the membranes of the spinal cord usually occuring in conjunction with cerebral meningitis.

The patient complains of shooting pains in

72

the limbs and body, excessive sensitivity of the skin, rigors, rapid pulse and fever. The limbs are rigid, the head is retracted and the spinal area is very tender. Complete bed rest with ice packs to the spine and morphine injections were standard treatment but most cases were ultimately fatal.

spinner's cancer cancer of the scrotum.
Twenty per cent of all cases of cancer of the scrotum occur in mule-spinners in the cotton trade. It is caused by chronic irritation from friction against the faller bar of the machine and oil saturating the spinners' clothes.

spirochaetosis infection by the group of bacteria known as spirochaetes some of which are responsible for syphilis.

spotted fever term used for both typhus and cerebro-spinal fever.

spurious pregnancy phantom or imagined pregnancy
It usually occurs when a woman has a desperate desire to have children

sputum saliva and mucous secretions from the nose or lower air passages which is spat out of the mouth.

St. Anthony's fire (see erysipelas).

St. Vitus dance (see chorea).
In the 15thC. the population of Strasburg was attacked by a peculiar nervous affliction and the sufferers made pilgrimages to the shrine of St. Vitus. Faith and exercise cured them.

stampe to pound or crush in a mortar with a pestle to extract juice.

starting sudden awakening from sleep by pain or irritation.
It often occurs in children during teething.

stethescope instrument for detecting sounds in the chest.
It was invented in 1816 by Lannec, a Frenchman, and his first effort was a sheet of rolled up paper.

still-born child born after the 28th week of pregnancy but which does not take a breath at birth.
Since 1907 all children born after the 28th week of pregnancy must be registered at the local Register Office of Births, Marriages and Deaths and may not be buried without a certificate saying that the child was not born alive.

stink damp (see choke damp).

stools (see faeces) healthy people were advised to 'go to stool each morning'.

strangulated hernia when the blood supply to the hernia is cut off and faecal matter builds up leading to necrosis, infection and death.

strangulated ventral hernia (see above) ventral means relating to the abdomen.

strangury spasmodic contractions of the neck of the bladder or inflammation of the urethra which causes urine to be passed very slowly and painfully drop by drop.
In addition before, during and after urination there is severe agony and the paitient is troubled by a constant and urgent necessity to pass urine. This may occur every few minutes but never relieves the discomfort. It is due to acute infection of the bladder, bladder stones or gonorrhoea. Hippocrates noted that if the condition was accompanied by a fever and a twisting of the urethra, death would take place in seven days.

stricture narrowing of a canal or hollow organ such as the urethra or oesophagus, the result of inflammation or disease in its walls or occasionally from external pressure from a tumour.
It can be temporary or permanent depending upon the cause.

struma an old term for swellings in the neck used either for enlargement of the thyroid (see goitre) or tubercular swellings (see scrofula).

strumous old term used to describe tubercular disease.

stye infection of the glands in the eyelids which causes pain and inflammation.

suffocation failure to inhale enough air to keep the systems of the body alive.

sugar-flux (see diabetes).

summer diarrhoea (see intestinal catarrh).

suppressed measles a case of very mild or not well defined measles.

suppression of the menses stoppage of the monthly blood flow in females.

It is usually due to pregnancy but can also be caused by cancer in the ovaries or womb.

suppression/retention of urine inability of kidneys to secrete urine due to disease.

The symptoms begin with blood-stained urine passed in small amounts and the patient becomes nauseous and drowsy. After a few days the drowsiness passes off and the patient becomes anxious, restless and breathless with great muscular debility and twitching. A tight heavy feeling occurs in the area of the kidneys and gradually the pulse becomes slow and irregular, the tongue becomes sticky and coated and the skin cold and clammy. The abdomen swells and the patient becomes very pale. Vomiting and retching occur and attempts at passing urine only result in the passage of a few drops of blood. These symptoms gradually increase but death sometimes does not occur for up to three weeks.

suppuration the formation and discharge of pus from an infected wound, sore or ulcer.

suppurative cholecystitis formation of pus in an infected or diseased gall bladder.

surfeit (see dysentery).

surgical scarletina fever, red rash and enlarged glands which sometimes occurs along with septic conditions such as burns, empyema and abscesses.

surgical kidney widespread infection of the kidney.

swamp fever (see malaria).

swelling of the head (see hydrocephalus).

sweating sickness a disease that appeared in Europe and especially England during the 15thC. and 16thC. Profuse sweating was the most prominent symptom which caused extreme prostration and was always fatal (see plague).

swooning fainting (see syncope).

syncope very brief cessation of the heart beat resulting in loss of consciousness – fainting.

It is caused by powerful emotion, extreme pain, prolonged standing which causes the blood pressure to fall, disgusting smells and sights, breathing of bad air and general exhaustion or heart disease. The faint usually lasts only a few seconds or minutes but may last for hours and hysterical persons may pass from one faint to another several times in succession. The cessation of the heart may also be so complete that death occurs and fatal cases have been noted from the drinking of large quantities of cold water by a person who is hot from exertion.

synovial rheumatism a rheumatic condition in which an accumulation of fluid occurs in the synovial sacs especially those of the knee joints.

syphilis highly infectious venereal disease, contracted by sexual intercourse with an infected person, which can cause lesions in any part of the body.

The most prolonged of all contagious diseases, it lingers in the system and creeps into every nook and crevice of the body. It can be hereditary to the third and fourth generations. Symptoms include painful swellings in the groin, pains in the head and joints, scabs and dry scaly areas on various parts of the body especially the head which are a yellowish colour and resemble a honeycomb. Ulcers begin in the throat and spread to the inside of the mouth and then to the nose where they destroy the cartilege. Bones become brittle and break easily or become soft and bend like wax. Hard

swellings appear in the neck, armpits and groin and the eyes are affected with itching, pain, redness and sometimes total blindness. Eventually all normal functions of the body are disturbed, the face becomes pale, the body wasted and the patient falls into atrophy and dies. Women with syphilis who become pregnant in the late stages of the disease, 'bring children into the world that have universal erysipelas, are half rotten and covered with ulcers'.

Syphilis of the brain begins with intolerable violent headaches which are followed by sleeplessness, excitement, inability to think, weakness of memory, hallucinations and illusions. The disease spreads to the nerves causing double vision, paralysis of the mouth, difficulty in speaking, drooping of the eyelids, complete paralysis of most of the facial nerves, severe vertigo, staggering gait with walking only possible when supported on both sides.
The disease was first noted in 1494 when there was a severe, widespread outbreak among French soldiers involved in the siege of Naples. It was a common venereal disease in the 17^{th}C. and 18^{th}C. and the organism responsible for syphilis was not discovered until 1905. In 1964 there were 1381 new cases in England and Wales attending clinics for treatment and 791 deaths directly attributable to syphilis.

syphilitic meningitis occurs within the first 4 years of being infected with syphilis.
It is characterised by headache, paralysis of the facial nerves, hydrocephalus, vomiting, sleepiness and mental instability.

tabes dorsalis (see ataxy).

tabes mesenterica tuberculosis of the lymphatic glands of the mesentery in the abdomen.
The disease is seen chiefly in children characterised by chronic wasting of the body and caseous degeneration of the glands.

tachycardia rapid heart beat caused by many different diseases such as heart failure, anaemia, or by an infection or severe pain.

TB tuberculosis. Also known as phthysis; scrofula; Kings evill.

talipes deformity of the foot present at birth.
The ankle joint is twisted preventing the sole of one or both feet from touching the ground. Several varieties of the deformity exist and are caused by arrested development of the foetus or an abnormal position in the womb. It was once thought to be caused by the mother having a fright whilst she was pregnant. The condition occurring today can usually be cured by surgery.

tapeworms are flat, white and up to 12 meters in length like a piece of tape. *Their head is the size of a pin head which is equiped with suckers and sometimes tiny hooks to enable them to cling on to the walls of the bowel. They are caught by eating infected meat such as pork, beef or lamb and can live for between 10-30 years. Some species of the worm escape through the walls*

Fig. 114 –Taenia Solium (Pork Tapeworm).

75

of the intestines and are carried by the blood stream to organs such as the liver, lungs, kidneys and brain where they form cysts which increase in size eventually proving fatal to the host.

teething (see dentition).

terminally ill the last few weeks or months before death, the time when the only treatment is palliative care i.e. making the patient comfortable, rather than curing them.

The terminally ill can suffer many unpleasant symptoms including pain, weakness, fatigue, nausea, vomiting, anorexia, constipation, breathing difficulties, a dry mouth and fear.

tertian ague an ague which returns every other day.

tetanus infection of a wound by the tetanus bacillus found in soil and manure.

Once in the wound the infection spreads quickly to the nervous system causing loss of normal movement due to uncontrollable spasms of the muscles.

The victim lies with jaws tightly clenched, rigid neck, head drawn back, the face distorted in a fixed snarling grin showing the teeth. The back and abdominal muscles are in a constant state of rigid contraction and the limbs are bent and fixed. The slightest stimulus of light, sound or touch sets up violent and agonising spasms of the muscles with the result that rupture of these may occur. The patient never loses consciousness but the spasms give rise to exhaustion and the inability to breathe, death ensues quickly. The bacteria, discovered in 1884, are very resistant to heat and cold and can withstand drying for many years before developing into a new lethal bacteria . It can only develop and grow in the absence of oxygen. Hippocrates (400 BC) refers to the rapidly fatal disease of tetanus but thought it was brought on by the cold. A vaccine to prevent tetanus was discovered in 1890 and introduced as a childhood vaccine in 1927.

tetanus neonatorum tetanus of the newborn caused by infection of the stump of the umbilical cord.

It is caused by the bacteria entering the blood stream through the umbilicus of a new born child. The umbilical cord was often cut with a dirty knife, scissors or broken glass or could be tied with any bit of old string.

On the island of St. Kilda in the north Atlantic Ocean, the practice of applying sheep and cow dung to the umbilicus at birth to aid healing led to the decline of the population as four out of five babies died within 6-10 days after birth.

tetany undersecretion of the parathyroid glands leading to low levels of calcium in the bloodstream.

It is caused by injury or accidental removal of the glands during operations on the thyroid gland; by lack of vitamin D which is necessary to control the absorption of calcium from the bowel; or by the blood becoming too alkaline in consistency from

76

persistent vomiting or excessive overbreathing in cases of hysteria. Painful cramps occur in the feet and hands with the fingers rigidly extended and the thumbs pressed into the palms of the hands, convulsions, spasms of the windpipe causing choking and twitching of the face. Tetany is often seen in cases of rickets.

the pest (see black death).

the rose (see erysipelas).

thermometer medical thermometers have been in use since 1851 and early models used to take 15 to 20 mins to register a patient's temperature.

threadworms resembling a piece of thread around 6-12mm in length.

They live in large numbers in the lower bowel of infected persons particularly

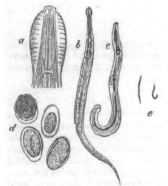

children. They cause great irritation particularly at night when the females emerge from the anus to lay around 10,000 eggs and then die. The eggs are then transferred to the nightclothes by the child scratching and then into the bedclothes, dust, toys and furniture as well as floating in the air. Eggs can survive for up to two months in these condition before hatching by which time the infection has been transferred to family and friends. Children often reinfect themselves by sucking their fingers after scratching.

three day fever (see dengue).

thrombosis thickening of the blood in the vessels leading to the formation of clots.

This occurs in certain conditions such as anaemia, cancer and poor circulation in the elderly. (see apoplexy).

thrush fungal infection of the mouth and pharynx but which may spread downwards to the stomach and intestines and can also occur in the genitala of women.

It is a common infection in newborn babies and young children and appears as small greyish-white distinctly raised points or scattered patches on the cheeks, tongue and lips which cannot be removed at first but later peel off to reveal a red bleeding ulcerated base. The mouth is very tender and dry and green diarrhoea, causing abdominal pain and sore buttocks, is present. The infant may refuse feeds and is generally very fretful and miserable.

The condition can also occur at the base of the fingernails in adults due to frequent wet working conditions.

It is now known to be a fungal infection but once thought to be only found in weak ill children suffering from diarrhoea, gastric catarrh and wasting. It was found to occur in older children in the last stages of tuberculosis, meningitis, typhoid or pneumonia. (see aphthae).

thyroid gland situated in front of the neck shaped like a horseshoe and containing many blood vessels.

It produces a hormone which is rich in iodine and necessary for the control of the metabolism. If the hormone is deficient in childhood, infants fail to grow (see cretinism), if in adulthood the patient becomes obese, lethargic and develops a coarse skin a condition known as myxoedema. If the gland is over-active the patient loses weight, has a rapid heart beat and a highly strung nervous temperament.

ticks blood sucking parasites usually found on animals which can transfer to a human host.

They are responsible for transmitting numerous diseases to man including typhus and cause intense itching and often inflamed areas on the 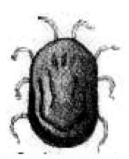 *skin. Tick bites are an occupational hazard of shepherds and gamekeepers.*

tinea capitas tinea favus or honeycomb ringworm of the scalp.

The condition usually occurs in children and is highly contagious. It is a human species of fungus but can be caught from domestic animals and horses. Severe cases cause a peculiar foetid, mouse-like odour which is characteristic of the disease. Scattered all over the scalp are circular patches of lusreless, greyish broken hairs and the skin itself is covered with greyish white scabs. In severe cases, a crusty patch of dead cells can appear which when lifted reveal a damp 'boggy' pus filled area underneath. Until it comes away the crusty patch can be very tight and cause pain but once loosened further infections can enter. Within this offensive mass lice, maggots etc breed. The disease easily extends to the lobes of the ears and into the canal of the ear in the form of red cracked skin, weepy or scaly or coated with scabs. The nostrils may be affected and their openings plugged with thick scabs, the skin of the upper lip being red and swollen. Eyelids and eyebrows are also often involved in the disease.

tinea pedis athlete's foot, scaly itchy patches between the toes with redness and cracks in the skin. Is very infectious and can lead to cellulitis or erysipelas.

tonsillitis inflammation of the tonsils occurring particularly between October and March and a frequent precursor of diseases such as measles or scarlet fever. *A sudden pain when swallowing is followed by chilliness and fever. The pain may spread to the ears and the glands under the jaws may be swollen.*

toothache a symptom of several problems of the teeth and gums, the pain of which may vary from very slight to great agony.

The most common cause is dental caries due to decay of the dentine which forms the bulk of the tooth under the outer covering of enamel. The teeth share in the general state of health and digestive disturbances, general debility and pregnancy render persons much more liable to toothache than when they are in ordinary health. Toothache is as old as history and decayed teeth have been found in Bronze Age skeletons. William Buchan writing in 1781 says 'This disease is so well known that it needs no description' and he ascribes the cause to obstructed perspiration or by neglecting some part of the usual covering of the head. The build up of tartar (lime salts) from uncleaned teeth was said to be the cause of more lost teeth than all other dental disorders combined. It renders the gums so sensitive that brushing is discarded and it then accumulates rapidly making the gums spongy and easy to bleed. The tartar then works its way under the gum causing the teeth to lose their support and they drop out. It also renders the breath exceedingly offensive. In 1971 only 50% of British children had caries-free teeth and 50% of over 35's had lost all their teeth. In Scotland the same year 44% of over 16's had lost all their teeth.

toxaemia blood poisoning.

It can occur in the later stages of pregnancy with vomiting, high blood pressure, oedema and headache. If uncontrolled by strict bed rest in a darkened room, permanent kidney damage or death may result.

toxic absorption the absorption of a poisonous substance through the skin.

It can be through long exposure to a toxic substance (see phossy jaw)*, or from injuries such as burns which become infected.*

toxic epidermal necrolysis severe form of bullous impetigo.
In this condition the blebs are very large and the infection damages the outer layer of skin which becomes loose and peel off in sheets leaving large raw area's of skin.

toxin poisonous substance from plant or animal cells or manufactured by the germs themselves such as diphtheria or tetanus.

toxoid non poisonous modification of a toxin used to immunise people against the disease.

trachea tube of cartilage and membrane extending from the back of the throat to the top of the lungs.
It is otherwise known as the windpipe.

tracheal diphtheria old term for croup.

tracheotomy surgical opening of the windpipe.
The operation is performed to enable the patient to continue breathing when the trachea is blocked by either disease or a foreign body. It has been performed successfully since the 1840's.

transverse myelitis a term used to describe severe damage to the spinal cord caused by lesions pressing on it. *Acute compression arises from fractures or dislocations of the spine, haemorrhage and thrombosis due to high blood pressure or syphilis. There is complete loss of sensation and paralysis of the legs and trunk with either incontinence of urine or the inability to pass urine due to paralysis of the muscles and pressure sores develop very quickly.*
Slow compression (see spinal caries).

trench fever (see typhus).

trench foot damage to the skin, surface blood vessels, nerves and muscles due to prolonged exposure to damp and cold resulting in a moist gangrenous looking condition of the skin.
This affection was very common on the Flanders Front during the first two winters of the Great War. Soldiers rarely removed their boots and socks when on front line duties and the trenches were often filled with water. When the use of gum boots and the daily drying of feet became compulsory, the incidence of trench foot fell rapidly.

tubercle 1. a small solid swelling similar to but larger than a pimple. **2.** a lesion produced by the tubercle bacillus containing white blood cells and abnormal tissue cells.

tuberculosis chronic infectious disease usually involving the lungs but can occur in any other part of the body e.g. the bones, tissues or other organs. Also known as TB; phthisis; scrofula; Kings evill.
Symptoms include fever, severe weight loss, cough with copious amounts of mucus, chest pain or coughing up blood. There are references to tuberculosis in India and America in 2000 BC and evidence of the disease has been found in Egyptian mummies. In the 5thC. BC Hippocrates described phthisis as the most widespread disease of the time and commented that it was always fatal. In the 17thC. and 18thC. tuberculosis was responsible for approximately one fifth of all the deaths in London and 50% of deaths in gaols. It was said to attack young persons between the ages of 15-30 of a slim build with a long neck, high shoulders and flat breasts. The disease was prevalent in England more than any other part of the world and this was said to be due to the great use of animal food, strong liquors, the general application to sedentary employment and the great quantity of pit-coal used. A vaccine to prevent infection by the disease was discovered in 1906 but despite this in England in 1974 there were 704 deaths from pulmonary tuberculosis and 453 deaths from other forms of the disease. Routine vaccination of schoolchildren in the UK was discontinued in 2006. If contracted today, the treatment lasts for 6 months.

tuberculosis meningitis caused by the tuberculosis bacteria and usually affected children under 10 years of age. *It was especially associated with improper feeding, malnutrition, poor hygiene or childhood* diseases such as measles and whooping cough. The symptoms include fatigue, listlessness, loss of appetite, headache and the child becomes peevish and irritable. This is followed by vomiting, constipation, intolerance of light and sound and the headache becomes severe causing the child to scream with a peculiar cry. The neck is so rigid that the head cannot be bent forward and the legs are similarly affected. Convulsions, paralysis and coma occur and death follows suddenly in a fit or from exhaustion.

tubular foetation (see ectopic pregnancy).

tumefaction swelling.

tumour an abnormal mass caused by excessive multiplication of cells.
The term is usually used to describe a cancerous mass.

turgescence becoming swollen or engorged.

turner's lung (see pneumoconiosis and grinder's asthma).

tussis (see whooping cough).

twilight sleep an injection of pain killing morphine and muscle relaxant scopolamine which was once used in child-birth.
The injection was administered hourly until the child was delivered or the mother was unconscious and pain free.

tympanitis inflammation of the ear drum and inner ear caused by infection.
If untreated by antibiotics it can cause a perforation of the ear drum.

typhoid fever caused by drinking infected water or food washed in infected water
It is characterised by a slowly rising fever, headaches, nosebleeds, weakness and fatigue, the presence of rose coloured spots on the abdomen and 'pea soup' diarrhoea often containing blood and shreds of tissue. The abdomen is distended and tender and by the end of the first week the patient is severely ill with a dry mouth and hot skin. Complications are common and include internal haemorrhage, perforation of the bowels, broncho-pneumonia, arthritis and heart failure. In severe cases bacteria settle in the liver and intestines and, until the discovery of antibiotics and a vaccine in 1896, patients died within three weeks. In 1907 Mary Mallon, known as Typhoid Mary, was the first American carrier of the disease to be identified and traced. Approximately 5% of people who contract typhoid continue to carry and pass on the disease after they recover. A vaccine was produced and used in 1907 for the protection of the British troops in the South African War and in India.

typhus fever the organism responsible originated in rats but was transmitted from rat to rat and rat to man by fleas and lice and once established in the human community was spread by lice.

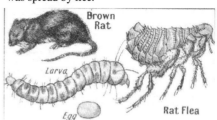

It began with a very high temperature, nausea, headache, weakness, inflamed eyes and a great dejection of mind, the same symptoms as influenza which it was often mistaken for but within 4-5 days the patient broke out in a pink rash which later turned purple or brown. This was followed by severe headaches, delirium, the muscular tissues of the heart became softened and death ensued. There were several instances of gangrene of the genitals accompanying typhus fever in which the blackened, dry end of the penis dropped off after a few days and the stump healed. The disease was highly infectious in any overcrowded places, slums, jails, asylums ships, etc. It often assumed epidemic proportions as in WWI and II and was often seen during periods of famine. In 1781 it was being blamed on foul air from overcrowding or from putrid animal or vegetable effluvia poisoning the air.

typhus nervosa a milder form of typhus described in 1875 as slow fever or low fever.

It was observed in 1868 as being characterised by slight shiverings, heavy vertiginous headache and nausea, sighings, despondency and peculiar expressions of anxiety, coma or quiet delirium.

ulcer (1) an open discharging sore area on the skin which takes more than 6 weeks to heal.

Usually found on the leg or foot and caused by diseased veins or arteries, diabetes, rheumatoid arthritis, lymphoedema, injury, infection, tuberculosis or malignancies.

(2) Internal ulcers can be caused by age, stress, heredity, excessive amounts of acid in the stomach, irritation or malignancies.

ulcerative stomatitis inflammation of the mucous membrane lining the mouth caused by bacteria.

This is a more serious condition than either catarrhal or aphthous stomatitis and the ulcers extend along the margin of the gum surrounding the teeth. The breath is foul and the patient is generally very unwell.

undulent fever (see brucellosis).

uraemia build up of waste products in the blood due to the end stages of any kidney disease.

The symptoms occur very gradually with the patient feeling fatigued and exhausted. Anaemia is usually present and, as the patient becomes increasingly drowsy, vomiting and diarrhoea occur sometimes accompanied by continuous hiccoughing. The drowsiness is then followed by coma and twitchings and convulsions occur before death.

uraemic convulsions similar to an epileptic fit but the breath smells of urine due to the accumulation of urinary products in the blood.

Usually occurs in the terminal stages of kidney disease.

urticaria skin condition of intensely irritating elevated wheals or welts appearing in crops over the surface of the skin.

It normally disappears within a day or two but is usually associated with an allergy to food, sunlight, drugs etc. and, if the cause is not identified and removed, repeated exposure will cause worsening symptoms.

uterine cancer cancer of the womb

Until the operation of hysterectomy was perfected in the 19thC., the treatment for this disease consisted of passing tubes into the womb to puncture the tumour and relieve the abdominal swelling. This painful procedure resulted in the release of copious amounts of offensive fluid but brought much temporary relief. It had to be performed several times over a period of six months until the death of the patient.

vaccinate to inject a solution containing living or dead bacteria or virusus to raise the body's own resistance against future infection with the disease.

Although the organisms are killed by heat this does not totally destroy their toxins.

V.D.H. valvular disease of the heart (see mitral disease and aortic disease).

valvulitis inflammation of a valve, term usually used in connection with a heart valve.

vapour bath the area surrounding the patient is kept moist by means of the steam from a permanently boiling kettle (see bronchitis kettle).

It is used in cases of bronchitis with a bronchitis kettle or fish kettle. The bed or cot of the patient was enveloped in sheeting with the long spout of the kettle pumping steam inside.

varicella (see chicken pox).

veins blood vessels which convey blood from the tissues back to the heart.

The larger veins have valves to stop the backward flow of blood which is dark red due to the lack of oxygen. If severed the blood flows from a vein in a stream as it is forced back to the heart not pumped.

venereal disease highly infectious diseases caught through sexual intercourse.

Syphilis, gonorrhea and chancroid were once the most common but today chlamydia tops the list.

ventral hernia occurring in the abdomen.

vertigo loss of the power of balance.

The person has a false sensation as to his own movements or to those of surrounding objects. Caused by a disturbance of the fluid in the internal ear by turning quickly or falling or jumping. Severe and sudden vertigo is caused by Meniere's Disease in which there is loss of function of the inner ear and occasionally sudden haemorrhage will occur causing an apoplectic-like fall of great violence. The condition can also be caused by heart disease or brain tumours.

vesicle an elevation of the upper horny layer of skin by fluid accumulated between it and the deeper layers.

It is of the size of a pimple and the fluid is clear or milky. The thin covering may burst and the fluid escape, or it may evaporate, or the clear fluid may become yellow and a pustule is formed.

Vincent's angina bacterial infection of the throat.

The throat becomes inflamed and ulcerated and the breath foul smelling.

virus micro-organisms which cause infections such as influenza, poliomyelitis, smallpox.

viscera general name given to the large organs within the chest and abdomen.

vitiligo patches of skin which have no pigment or colouring and are completely white.

vomiting regurgitation of the contents of the stomach.

This is one of the first signs of disease or infection before the true cause becomes apparent and is present in many terminal illnesses. Vomiting often exhausts a patient, causes dehydration and anorexia due to fear of vomiting (See pyloric stenosis).

Voneconomo's disease (see encephalitis lethargica).

wandering pneumonia onset of pneumonia spreading very slowly from the apex to the base of a lung then gradually spreads to the opposite side.

It is usually seen in children.

war fever an epidemic of typhus.

war shock psycho-neurotic symptoms that were engendered as a result of the strain of warfare.

Many of the worst cases occurred behind the lines without any exposure to shock or injuries and the symptoms corresponded with those of hysteria. The patient was full of anxious dread associated with different physical phenomena such as paralysis mutism, deafness, loss of sight, insomnia, headache, indigestion, exhaustion, loss of memory, 'soldiers heart', hysterical vomiting and fits among many others.

wasting (see marasmus).

water in the head (see hydrocephalus).

water on the brain or watery brain (see hydrocephalus).

In the mid 19thC.. it was said to be caused by blows to the head, constant irritation of the bowels from indigestible food, the straining coughs of long-continued whooping cough or the improper treatment of measles. It was mainly thought to stem from encouraging the child to learn reading and spelling at too early an age thereby the 'tender vessels of the head become inflamed from over-exertion and excitement'.

watchfulness/watching sleeplessness, insomnia.

In the 5thC. BC Hippocrates recognised that if disease exists, watchfulness was excessive.

water-brash heartburn or indigestion where bitter bile products regurgitate from the stomach into the mouth.

water canker (see cancrum oris).

waxy degeneration (see amyloid disease).

wesand (see trachea).

white damp (see after damp).

white death pulmonary tuberculosis.

white leg a form of phlebitis in the veins of the leg or thigh after childbirth.

This condition can occur up to two weeks after delivery and was common until the mid 20thC. as women were kept in bed for at least two weeks after delivery. The leg becomes swollen, very painful, oedematous and white due to the interruption of the circulation. Collapse would follow suddenly and the face, lips and extremities would turn blue. A semi-conscious state would last for a few hours before the patient died.

white plague (see tuberculosis).

white swelling tuberculosis of the joints.

whooping cough or hooping cough, infectious childhood disease characterised by a spasmodic cough which ends with a distinctive whoop often followed by an attack of vomiting.

An attack usually lasts over six weeks and the disease is more severe and fatal in very young children. Complications such as broncho-pneumonia, convulsions, bronchiectasis and gastro-enteritis were common before routine immunisation began in 1952.

wildfire (see erysipelas).

witch's milk watery, milk like fluid expressed from the breasts of newborn babies of either sex.

The breasts become tense and hard due to excess hormones from the mothers circulation. If left alone the condition will subside spontaneously. However it was once common practice pre 19thC. for midwives to squeeze the breasts to express the fluid which then lead to inflammation and sometimes infection which would be fatal to the child.

woolsorter's disease (see pulmanory anthrax).

worm fever illness caused when a patient is infested with worms.

The symptoms of worm infestation described in 1781 are paleness of the countenance or at times universal flushing of the face, grinding of the teeth in sleep, swelling of the upper lip, diarrhoea, sour or stinking breath, a hard swelled belly, a great thirst, frothy urine, pains in the side with a dry cough, drowsiness, cold sweats, palsy, epileptic fits and many other unaccountable nervous symptoms which were formerly attributed to witchcraft or the influence of evil spirits.

worms (see threadworms, roundworms, tapeworms).

yeaxing (see hiccoughing).

yellow atrophy of the heart occurs when the muscular tissue of the heart is transformed into fat.

The deposits of fat globules become more abundant and the muscular fibres grow pale, then yellowish and lastly whitish and bacony. The tissues lose their firmness and grow friable and rotten.

yellow fever an acute viral infection transmitted to man from the mosquito.

Occurs on the east and west coasts of America, the West Indies and Africa. The mortality from the disease is always very great, more particularly among the young and robust and it was very fatal among armies and navies. The symptoms appear suddenly with a feeling of weakness, faintness and restlessness followed by a high fever, flushes in the face, gasping for cool air, white tongue, vomiting, excessive thirst, redness, heaviness and burning of the eyes, darting pains in the head and small of the back. These symptoms may last up to 3 days and are followed by lessening of the fever, soft clammy skin, small quantities of very dark coloured urine and a yellow tinge to the eyes which eventually extends all over the body. The vomit becomes very dark (see black vomit) and frequent, and bleeding can occur from the mouth, nose, eyes or stomach and exhaustion becomes great and the patient dies within 10-14 days.

Sometimes the disease proceeds so rapidly that the patient is carried off within 24 hours.

yellow jack (see yellow fever).

Non-Medical terms for causes of death

They are extracted from numerous registers and certificates.
This is a list of causes commonly used but which are not actual medical terms.

abscess of thigh this is almost certainly a case of tuberculosis of the hip as in the late 19thC it was claimed that the vast majority of cases of hip disease progressed to an abscess in the joint.

abscess of neck usually associated with tuberculosis of the glands under the lower jaw. The whole neck may be involved and there is great swelling with marked prostration of the patient. Sometimes there is difficulty in breathing or talking due to the pressure of the pus filled abscess on surrounding structures.

abscess of liver or gall bladder occasionally found in tuberculosis of the liver or from the absorption of septic material from an abscess in any area of the abdomen. Sometimes abscesses in the liver are secondary to typhoid ulcers or to the irritation of worms which have penetrated into the bile ducts.

abscess of lung usually caused following the inhalation of a foreign body into the lung or by septic matter from the nose or throat dripping into the lung. There is a persistent coughing up of copious amounts of foul-smelling bloodstained sputum. The condition was fatal before the discovery of antibiotics.

after vaccination the first vaccine for smallpox was taken from the pustules of a recently diseased patient and if they were also suffering from undiagnosed syphilis this would be passed on to the recipient. Erysipelas may also be transferred in the same way in which case redness of the arm and fever occur on the 2nd or 3rd day, or the virus may accidentally gain entrance after the pustule caused by the vaccination has matured. In this case the symptoms of erysipelas occur on the 7th – 10th day. Encephalitis is rare in infants but can occur in older children or adults with severe headaches, fever, vomiting and convulsions. Death is common in all these cases.

a lingering disorder could be any illness which was fatal until the discovery of its cause in the late 19^{th}C or 20^{th}C, e.g. diabetes, cancer, tuberculosis, heart disease.

a lingering illness as above.

asphasia this term is likely to be a mis-spelling of either asphyxia or aphasia.

autumnal diarrhoea typhoid fever - Hippocrates noted that diseases during the autumn are very severe and destructive.

bitten by hound this is a bite or savaging from a dog which had rabies or from an infection in the ensuing wound(s).

breathing problems either asthma or heart failure.

burns and scalds in the 19thC these were described as exceedingly fatal due to shock, pain, lung complications (pneumonia) and cerebral effusion (oedema).

cardiac failure due to faulty infiltration this is probably a mis-spelling of fatty infiltration.

clot on brain a stroke.

cold as this person was only 34 years old he could have had influenza or be suffering from hypothermia.

congenital cirrhosis of the liver cirrhosis arises from alcholism and is therefore unlikely to be present at birth. However deformity or absence of the bile ducts at birth leads to a form of cirrhosis from which the child may die due to a haemorrhage from the navel or intestines during the first few days of life. If the child survives for a few months it will be severely jaundiced, the faeces are very pale but internal bleeding will subsequently make the stools black and the skin will be covered in bruises. All cases are fatal within a few months.

cot death the term applied to the unexpected death of an apparently healthy baby while it is asleep. Many theories abound but still today no definite cause has been found . Historically babies most likely to die in this way were ones who were underweight at birth and came from large, poor families.

decay of nature a gentle way of describing old age.

decline gradual loss of general health and strength, a progressive weakening of all the physical processes of the body – a descent towards death. The word is not usually applied to the process of natural decay associated with old age but generally refers to the failing vitality of young men and women suffering from any disorder which slowly and steadily enfeebles the whole body. Could be any number of chronic diseases such as anaemia, tuberculosis, diabetes or asthma.

deficient circulation poor circulation due to causes such as anaemia, heart failure or diabetes. If the patient then caught an infection it would be difficult to eradicate as the body would not be receiving enough nutrients and oxygen to fight the infection.

deformed mouth either a hare lip and cleft palate or a deformity due to the result of congenital syphilis both of which would have led to the baby being unable to suck at the breast and would therefore die from malnutrition.

diaphragmatic pleurisy and jaundice pleurisy makes breathing painful as the diaphragm moves with each breath. The jaundice would be caused by a liver infection so the possiblity is that this was a disease such as TB or cancer.

disease of earbone this would mean mastoiditis

enlarged mammae this term was applied to a 17 year old male and during puberty congestion can occur in the breasts of both boys and girls causing swelling and tenderness. Very occasionally this can lead to the formation of an abscess.

fluid on brain this would usually refer to hydrocephalus.

fracture of hip/thigh osteoporosis or thinning of the bones takes place in both men and women after middle age and more severely in smokers. Although a fracture in itself would not cause death the resulting prolonged period of inactivity would predispose the patient to hypostatic pneumonia from which they would die.

from a wasp sting this would be a severe allergic reaction known as anaphylactic shock which is the body's immediate response to sensitization with a foreign substance. The patient would be covered in an urticarial rash, with severe oedema causing breathing difficulties, and shock and death would occur rapidly.

gastric irritation possibly inflammation of the stomach due to an ulcer or infection.

general debility self-explanatory but the gentleman in question was 83 years old.

general/gentle decay old age. The Bible tells us that man's alloted span is 'three score years and ten' and in the run up to this period signs of ageing become apparent. The tissues of the body become rigid and lose their elasticity, the bones become brittle and break more easily, ligaments become stiff making movement slow and painful. During middle life fat is often deposited beneath the skin but is absorbed again in old age leaving the skin wrinkled. The skin becomes thin and less well lubricated causing it to be easily bruised and grazed and its blood vessels do not react properly to heat or cold therefore cold becomes more acutely felt.   The walls of the larger blood vessels become thicker and then brittle causing obstructions or haemorrhages leading to heart attacks or strokes. The lens of the eyes loose their elasticity leading to gradual loss of sight and if not already missing by this time the teeth fall out!

griping of the guts this would be severe diarrhoea or dysentery.

haemorrahge from navel as this child was only a few hours old it is possible that the umbilical cord was not tied properly at birth and the child was then wrapped up but slowly bled to death.

haemorrhage at birth possibly the same cause as above.

haemorrhage from navel/exhaustion possibly from same cause as above.

haemorrhage from the scalp The face and head bleed profusely when wounded. This was probably a scalp wound from a fall or a blow to the head from which the blood flow could not be staunched.

hard gums-livid probably a baby that was teething.

hardened left lobe of lung most probably due to tuberculosis.

heart failure from distended stomach this child was 9 years old therefore the most probable cause would be peritonitis or a tumour causing ascites in the abdomen which would in turn put a strain upon the heart eventually leading to heart failure.

heart spasm probably a heart attack or a stroke.

imperfect bowel see imperforate anus.

imperfect heart an imperfectly formed foetal heart – the child would be stillborn.

infantile diarrhoea see summer diarrhoea.

inflammation of the bowels presumably some pain or bleeding was present which could have been caused by polyps, diverticular disease or cancer.

inward/internal bleeding the patient would be either coughing up blood in which case the usual cause would be tuberculosis of the lungs or bleeding from the rectum which would be caused by polyps or cancer of the intestine. Vomiting blood would indicate a stomach ulcer.

inward obstruction usually a cancerous tumour blocking the intestine.

leather bottle stomach this is most probably a case of chronic gastritis commonly caused by overeating, alcohol excess or secondary to other diseases such as cirrhosis of the liver or heart failure. Symptoms include loss of appetite, pain or discomfort after eating with bloating of the abdomen and frequent vomiting.

Frequent attacks result in chronic irritation of the lining of the stomach and, after a long period of irritation, the secreting structures of the stomach atrophy leaving no gastric juices to digest the food. The interior of the stomach becomes constantly coated with a tough mucus which also prevents digestion. The lining of the stomach is permanently congested and becomes thickened forming deep ridges and furrows. Frequent bleeding takes place from the dilated veins. In the later stages of the disease, thickening of other layers of the stomach takes place leading to increased impairment of digestion; a reduction in the size of the stomach with eventual blockage in the outlet from the stomach to the small intestine. The condition is found more often in women than in men and the incidence increases with age. Many patients also have long standing anaemia.

lingering illness this could be applied to any number of diseases such as tuberculosis, diabetes, cancer etc.

living a profligate life this 20 year old female was most probably a prostitute who died from a venereal disease or from cancer of the neck of the womb which is often caused by a sexually transmitted virus.

lung disease this could have been anything from tuberculosis or pneumonia to asthma all of which were fatal until the late 19C.

lymotic enteritis a probable mis-spelling of zymotic enteritis a term which covers all epidemic, endemic and infectious diseases.

mesmeric disease as mesmerism is hypnotism I think this is most probably a mis-spelling of mesenteric disease.

monstrosity there are many abnormalities which can affect a foetus during pregnancy resulting in the term monstrosity. Sometimes only the lower trunk and legs are formed, the top of the skull may be missing or the foetus may have two necks and heads. The abdomen may be greatly distended or it is unformed and the intestines are hanging out. Some of these abnormalities are genetic, others caused by the mother's blood group being incompatible with the father's or by the mother having diabetes.

nervous apoplexy in 1792 some of the causes of apoplexy were said to be 'violent passions' such as anger or intense study.

non Viability this child was 10 hours old and would most probably have been many weeks premature.

nulls syphilitic this child was 8 months old and the term literally means 'no syphilis'. It is probable then that the mother suffered from the disease and the child died from malnutrition because she was not able to feed it.

obstruction of circulation term possibly used to indicate heart failure or arteriosclerosis.

obstruction / stoppage in the breast this cause of death was given for several children under the age of 2 years which possibly indicates that the mother had insufficient milk to feed them and they died from malnutrition. Alternatively it could be mastitis or inflammation of the breast. On the 3rd or 4th day of life a few drops of colourless fluid can be squeezed from the breasts of infants of either sex followed by a slight milky secretion for the next 2 to 3 weeks. This is caused by residual hormones from the mother reacting upon the breast tissue of the child and is harmless if left alone. (see witch's milk).

old and childish very literal description of senile dementia.

ossification of the heart literally means tissue turning to bone. Therefore this condition presumably means hardening of the veins and arteries within the heart.

overflowing of blood this 24 year old male could have had a ruptured main blood vessel due to an aneurism which is an area of enlargement of a major artery which grows progressivly larger until it bursts.

overloaded stomach large indigestible meals cause acute gastritis, inflammation of the stomach, which in turn causes loss of appetitie, nausea, vomiting, headache and giddiness with abdominal pain. Unless eating habits are modified the condition becomes chronic with frequent vomiting and abdominal distension.

pain between shoulders this is a classic symptom of a heart attack.

pain in ear death in this case would be caused by otitis media.

pretritis probably means temperal arteritis.

relaxed state probably means that the patient was weakened by a long illness or was in the last stages of a terminal illness.

retroversion chysterectomy this appears to be a mis-spelling of hysterectomy, surgical removal of the womb, a retroverted womb is not in itself dangerous but can cause painful menstrual periods.

rheumatic gout a term probably used due to the deformity of the joints in gout which look very similar to rheumatism.

rising in the lights lights is an old term for lungs so probably means pneumonia.

septic absorption this condition is cited in connection with either burns or scalds. The wounds would very quickly become infected and as the skin would be burnt away the infection would rapidly enter the blood stream causing septicaemia.

septic pneumonia probably acute pneumonia ending in an abscess or gangrene of the lung where the pneumonia infection is secondary to a pre-existing disease such as diabetes, Bright's Disease or old and partially healed tuberculosis of the lung.

sickly from birth possibly a premature baby or one whose mother had endured a long and difficult labour. Alternatively the child could have had congenital abnormalities making feeding difficult.

slain with a fall this suggests that the person would have been knocked unconscious and sustained severe head injuries or a broken neck.

snow and cold someone who had been lost or wandering on moors in the winter and died of hypothermia – severe loss of body heat leading to the slowing down and eventual cessation of all systems of the body.

spasm in chest this was probably a heart attack.

spasm of the throat this was most probably laryngismus stridius

sudden bleeding mouth this was either a ruptured aortic aneurism or a massive haemoptysis.

suddenly the wide variation of ages suggests that this could be anything from a cot death to a stroke or heart attack.

summer diarrhoea was a specific term given to infectious gastroenteritis in infants which was epidemic during the months of June and July.

sweating sickness term usually applied to epidemics of the plague.

syphilitis cachesoia probably means cachexia due to syphilis.

turned blue/purple in face probably caused by choking or apoplexy.

twisted bowel this is another name for a strangulated hernia

unsound mind suicide may be the result of severe mental depression and may be prompted by delusions of persecution or by hallucinations or hearing the sound of voices urging them to commit self harm. It may accompany acute illness or be the one outstanding feature of the illness, a true suicidal impulse. The idea is sometimes quite a sudden one, the patient after the attempt is quite unable to account for his actions. It is a cry for help rather than an intent to die or it could be a long held wish and the details of the suicide carefully planned.

visitation of God natural causes, the term suggests a sudden death such as a stroke.

vomiting blood see haemetemasis.

vomiting during sleep the most likely explanation is of severe alcohol intoxication and the inhalation of vomit into the lungs causing drowning.

water on chest see hydrothorax.

wearing the nearest explanation for this cause of death that can be found is 'weariness' which was said to be one of the symptoms of fever and smallpox. The ages of the deceased who died from this ranged from 3 years to 95 years so it could also have been a lingering illness such as tuberculosis or diabetes.

white jues this reference in was to a child aged 2 years and is probably a mis-spelling of lues which was syphilis.

worn out at the age of 64. Self-explanatory in this case but of course could be from the effects of a long lasting illness, prolonged childbirth or just old age.

Bibliography

Blakiston's, **Pocket Medical Dictionary**, 4th Edition, (Ed. Ingo, Judith B.) 1979, McGraw-Hill Book Company, London.

Buchan, William, **Domestic Medicine or a Treatise on the Prevention & Cure of Diseases**, 7th Edition, 1781, W. Strahan & T. Cadell, London.

Buchan, William, **Domestic Medicine or a Treatise on the Prevention & Cure of** Diseases, 14th Edition, 1783, A. Strahan & T. Cadell, London.

Clarkson, Leslie, **Death, Disease And Famine,** (publishers proofs), 1975, Gill & Macmillan Ltd., Bristol.

Davis, T.R.C., **Journal of the British Society for Surgery of the Hand,** Vol. 26, Issue 5, October 2001, Editorial.

Doncaster Archive Department, **Doncaster Health Authority Death Registers, 1875 – 1929**.

Eagles, J.B., **John Benson Pritchett, First Medical Officer of Health for Huddersfield**, 1984, Huddersfield Local History Workshop.

Fry, John, and Sandler, Gerald, **Common Diseases, Their Nature, Presentation & Care,** 5th Edition, 1993, Kluwer Academic Publications.

Grundy, Joan E., **History's Midwives,** 2003, Federation of Family History Societies (Publications) Ltd.

Joint Committee of the Royal College of Physicians, **The Nomenclature of Diseases**, 1869, Spottiswoode & Co., London.

McGreggor-Robertson, J., **The Household Physician,** 2 vols: 1908, The Gresham Publishing Compnay, London.

Medical and Chirurgical Society, **Medico-Chirurgical Transactions, Vol 16,** 1830, Longman, Rees, Orme, Brown & Green, London.

Miller, Frank E; Hunt, H. Lyons; McCormick, F.J; Burr, Buchanan; King, Morris L; (Eds.) **Domestic Medical Practice,** 1930, Domestic Medical Society, Chicago, New York, London.

Morten, Honnor, **The Nurses Dictionary**, 15th Edition, (Ed. Taylor, Florence) 1935, Faber & Faber Ltd., London.

Robinson, Henry, **The Midwife's Pronouncing Dictionary & Encyclopaedia**, (Ed. Watson, J.K.) 1927, The Scientific Press, London.

Sajous, Charles E. de M., **Analytical Cyclopaedia of Practical Medicine,** 6 volumes, 5th revised edition, 1908, F.A. Davis Company, Philadelphia.

Smith, Leslie & Doreen, **Sudden Deaths in Suffolk 1767-1858,** 1995, Suffolk Family History Society.

Smith, Doreen, **More Sudden Deaths in Suffolk 1858-1921,** 2000, Suffolk Family History Society.

The Concise Home Doctor Encyclopedia of Good Health (undated but approx 1934), Amalgamated Press Ltd., London.

Thomson, William A.R., **Black's Medical Dictionary,** 31st Edition 1978, Adam & Charles Black, London.

Thoresby Society, **The Registers of the Parish of Adel 1606 – 1812**, (Ed. Lumb, George Denison), 1985, Leeds.

Toohey, Dr., **Medicine for Nurses**, 1964, 6th Edition (Ed. Bloom Arnold), E.& S. Livingstone Ltd., London.

Transactions of the Pathological Society of London, 16th Edition, 1865, Roche, Rotherhithe.

Transactions of the Provincial Medical and Surgical Association Vol: XIV, 1845, Deighton & Co. Worcester.

Various German Authors, **Clinical Lectures on subjects connected with Medicine and Surgery,** 1894, The New Sydenham Society, London.

Yorkshire Archaeological Society Parish Register Section, **The Parish Register of Scruton 1572 – 1837,** (Ed. Preston, C.S.), 1991, YAS, Parish Register Section.

Yorkshire Parish Register Society, **The Parish Register of Carlton-Juxta-Snaith 1598 – 1812,** (Ed. Kaye, Walter J.), 1934, The Yorkshire Parish Register Society.

Yorkshire Parish Register Society, **The Parish Register of Swillington Yorks, 1539 –1812,** (Ed. Kirk, George E), 1944, The Yorkshire Parish Register Society.

Medical Snippets

The cholera epidemic of 1832 claimed 31,376 lives in England, the total number of cases reported was 82,528.
Annals of Yorkshire, John Mayhall, 1878,
Simpkin, Marshall and Co., London.